*The Doctor and His Enemy*

1852

FORTITER

# The Doctor
# and His Enemy

ALAN WYKES

E. P. Dutton & Co., Inc.

NEW YORK          1966

*First published in the U.S.A. 1966 by E. P. Dutton & Co., Inc.*
*Copyright, ©, 1965 by Alan Wykes      All rights reserved.*
*Printed in the U.S.A.*      FIRST EDITION

# CONTENTS

# FOREWORD

The medical profession in Britain has an inviolable rule which precludes practising doctors from associating their names with any project that might gain them money, fame, patients, or even public recognition as individuals in their calling. This system, being traditional and the invention of doctors themselves, presumably has ethical advantages they approve of. It has no advantages for the writer who chooses to write about doctors, for he is forced to use anonyms or pseudonyms – hardly a good way of gaining his readers' confidence. But there it is.

I have chosen to make the doctor I am writing about here anonymous rather than pseudonymous because it seemed to me less likely to make an apparent fiction of his existence. I have called him simply 'the Doctor' throughout, but have allowed him physical characteristics, so that he has for the reader, I hope, a corporeal presence and isn't just a symbolic figure. Symbolism isn't my cup of tea. I am interested in applying my imagination to the presentation of people and facts.

You will find some people in this story who, not being doctors, have been given real names – some of them very familiar. Adolf Hitler is one of these. But let me say quickly to those who may be dismayed at the thought of yet another book about the infamous dictator, this isn't such a book. Hitler appears in the early pages then disappears, never to return. He is there because he was of particular interest to the Doctor as a subject of medical, rather than psychological, study.

The Doctor is one of the very few men in the world who have made a special study of venereal diseases. As you will see, venereology – plus its adjunctive study, sexology – wasn't his choice: circumstances combined to thrust it upon him. And having

9

accepted the challenge he made something more than the best of it: he became one of the minuscule number who know as much as there is to know, to date, about venereal diseases.

Venereal disease, then, is the 'enemy' of my title. There are in fact a number of venereal diseases and they are known euphemistically as 'the social diseases'. But the book is in no sense a moral tract. I have enjoyed writing about a specialist in a highly specialized profession and satisfying my curiosity about a subject that has offered many fascinations; and I have enjoyed tussling with the clarification of its complexity for the enlightenment of laymen such as myself. I also enjoy repeating, now, that the moral aspect of venereal disease is something about which I have tried to remain firmly objective. That the disease is associated with sexual intercourse is a fortuitous biological fact and has no more significance medically than that baldness is commoner in men than in women. From the viewpoint of conventional morals pneumonia or rabies would have the same social stigma attached to them if they were sexual diseases; and if they were sexual diseases that fact would be equally insignificant medically. Doctoring, I have confirmed for myself, is a calling inspired equally by compassion and curiosity. As individuals in a community doctors may, and often do, have strong views on sexual morality; but as healers they are indifferent to anything but healing.

Writing too is a calling concerned largely – not exclusively – with curiosity. And although I started off perfectly satisfied with my self-imposed brief to write solely about the Doctor as a doctor, I very quickly discovered that he is remarkable in other fields than medicine. I wasn't surprised. All people are remarkable if you observe them closely enough and listen to them without interrupting. I interrupted very little. I was well rewarded.

I am obliged to Mr H. Montgomery Hyde for giving me leave to quote, on p. 28, from his *The Trials of Oscar Wilde*.

A.W.

# PART ONE

# The Lesser Enemy

# 1    *A Quarrel in Vienna*

Three young men were returning to their lodging at 27 Meldemannstrasse, Vienna, on an April evening in 1910. The names of two of them, who are still alive and, in view of what I have to reveal about them, entitled to the privacy of incognitos, will be recorded here as Stefan and Daniel. The third is dead and has no lien on my social conscience anyway. His name was Adolf Hitler.

They were quarrelling over a girl, a Jewish whore whose name nobody remembers but who was an individual and therefore entitled to one. Hannah is as good and as Jewish as any.

Naturally enough neither Stefan nor Daniel recalls the dialogue of the quarrel; and equally naturally Hitler doesn't refer to the occasion in his autobiography *Mein Kampf*. But it was a fierce quarrel, as quarrels over women often are, and the nub of it was that Stefan and Daniel had shared Hannah between them for some weeks now and Hitler, who was already indebted to them for such hospitality as their circumstances allowed, had characteristically used the girl himself as if she were common property. In a sense, of course, she was. Harlots of Hannah's grading, which was extremely low, cannot claim the status of an exclusive mistress; the extent of their promiscuity is the key to their success (or tragedy, according to the viewpoint). But there is a distinct camaraderie among layabouts and vagabonds – a social stratum to which all three men at that time belonged – and one of the unwritten rules of this camaraderie had been violated. Hitler was being told a few home truths.

Naturally he wasn't accepting them. His was an unstable character compounded of idleness and idealism and resenting any kind of criticism. His normal reaction to any accusation of laziness was a lofty disdain that implied intense intellectual activity beyond the comprehension of the accuser; and if he was caught out in a solecism he would rant about the social structure being in a state of such complete chaos that individual conduct was a matter of utter insignificance.

The present matter of insignificance being his personal use of his friends' whore, he was justifying his behaviour by an outburst against the iniquity of living conditions in Vienna, the internal politics of the city's administration, and the moral and physical impurity of the Jews. Later he was to learn disastrously of this particular Jewess's impurity – she was a syphilitic in the early and acutely infectious stages of the disease – but at the moment his ranting had only the violent prejudice of opinions and observations that were not even original. He was a great absorber of second-hand opinions which he put through a third-rate brain and served up with fourth-rate oratory.

In the chapter in *Mein Kampf* entitled 'Years of Study and Suffering in Vienna' he omits to mention that his study was limited to rehashing other men's ideas, or that his suffering was caused by his own idleness; he mentions the various casual employments he supported himself by, not forgetting the watercolour views he painted and sold for trifling sums (but forgetting the showcards he painted for Teddy Perspiration Powder); and he has this, *inter alia,* to say about the Jews:

'Cleanliness, whether moral or of another kind, had its own peculiar meaning for these people. That they were water-shy was obvious on looking at them and, unfortunately, very often when not looking at them at all. The odour of those people in caftans often used to make me feel ill. Beyond that there were the unkempt clothes and ignoble exterior.

'All these details were certainly not attractive; but the revolting feature was that beneath their unclean exterior one suddenly perceived the moral mildew of the chosen race.

'What soon gave me cause for very serious consideration were the activities of the Jews in certain branches of life, into the mystery of which I penetrated little by little. Was there any shady undertaking, any form of foulness, especially in cultured life, in which at least one Jew did not participate? On putting the probing knife carefully to that kind of abscess one immediately discovered, like a maggot in a putrescent body, a little Jew who was often blinded by the sudden light.' (And he adds later in his interminable impugnation 'But a Jew can never be rescued from his fixed notions' – as choice an example of chucking stones out of glass houses as may be found.)

*Mein Kampf* was of course written years later and recorded the beginning of his hatred retrospectively, with the secret knowledge of his own syphilis and his megalomanic vision to give it bitterness. But there is plenty of evidence that his character was unstable before he went to Vienna – much of it in August Kubizek's story of their youthful friendship, *Young Hitler*. There, for example, it's recorded that in 1908 Hitler, with a fervour equal to that of the Women's Institute's singing of 'Jerusalem', redesigned the city of Linz – on paper. When Kubizek asked him where the money was to come from he replied by buying a lottery ticket. And when he failed to win a prize Kubizek says he had 'rarely heard him rage so madly as then. First he fumed over the State Lottery, this officially organized exploitation of human credulity, this open fraud at the expense of docile citizens. Then his fury turned against the State itself, this patchwork of ten or twelve, or God knows how many nations, this monster built up by Habsburg marriages. Could one expect other than that two poor devils should be cheated out of their last couple of crowns?'

There is also evidence that Hitler had somewhat small room to talk about the smell and appearance of Jews during his 'years of study and suffering' in Vienna. Rheinhold Hanisch, another roustabout who knew him there, says that he wore an ancient black overcoat (a gift from a Jew named Neumann) which reached below his knees, that his hair hung long over his collar from under a greasy black bowler hat, and that his thin face was covered with a black beard.

This is how Stefan and Daniel remember him too; they also

remember him sitting on the bed at 27 Meldemannstrasse naked while his clothes were being de-loused.

The establishment at Meldemannstrasse was euphemistically called a 'Men's Home', but it was no more than a dosshouse. It was situated in the Twentieth [north-east] District of the city, near the Danube, and on the night of the quarrel it was inhabited by the usual collection of tramps and drunks who dossed there whenever they could produce the money. By the time Hitler, Stefan, and Daniel got there that April night the quarrel had become extremely violent. Hitler's ravings had become incoherent and his companions' patience was exhausted. They pushed him into the dormitory, bashed him over the head and in the ribs, and flung him out into the street. He screamed imprecations at them and by way of reply they chucked down his inks, water colours, pens and brushes. That was the last they saw of him that night.

After an hour or so both Stefan and Daniel went out again, this time to find Hannah and bring her in from her beat. Her trade was mostly in doorways near the Nordwestbahnhof – a rapid but wearying trade sometimes involving four customers an hour (at fifty heller each, that is about threepence by 1910 values) and she no doubt found the dosshouse, with its lousy biscuit beds, comparatively comfortable and her customers Stefan and Daniel comparatively undemanding. They recall that she often stayed an hour or two (having bribed the janitor, who was the only person concerned with the No Women rule, with a few cigarettes on the way in) and then returned to her beat near the station.

On this particular evening they noticed that the faint rash they had seen on her body on the last occasion they had been with her had disappeared. She could hardly be called clean, but at least she no longer looked as if she had what they had thought might be heat rash or flea bites in the fading-out stage. It may seem naïve for two young men in their late teens and obviously promiscuous to suppose anything so innocent as flea bites on their consort; but although they had heard of venereal diseases their knowledge was vague, it certainly included nothing about the diseases' clinical manifestations, and even if it had they were living – existing, rather – in a manner that would have left them indifferent. If they had known on that evening that they were already incubating in their bodies the germs of syphilis transferred from Hannah on the occasion of their previous intercourse they would have been maliciously heartened to know too that Hitler also had been corrupted – and on the very occasion for which they had been lambasting him. Knowing nothing, they satisfied themselves in turn with Hannah, gave her the hundred heller or so they could scrape up between them, and turned her loose.

Hitler returned to lodge at the dosshouse a week or two later. Stefan and Daniel took no exception to this : they had worked their indignation off by beating him up and couldn't be bothered to extend their enmity. But they observed that when he took off his clothes to have them de-loused by baking in the dosshouse oven, he, like themselves, had a suspicion of a pink rash. They still didn't associate the rash with Hannah; nor did their general feeling of ill-being seem to them remarkable. They were not living the kind of life likely to encourage hundred per cent health; and when, after a while, the rash was accompanied by various other unpleasant manifestations they then wisely went to a doctor, and on being told the alarming diagnosis of syphilis were maliciously comforted when they recalled that Hitler had exhibited the same rash. By now he was probably in the same unpleasant state that they were in.

Soon after this their economic position improved and they were able to leave Vienna. They never saw Meldemannstrasse, or Hitler, again. Like everyone else, though, they had plenty of opportunity of hearing his clumping footsteps tramping through Germany.

# 2   A Meeting in Stuttgart

Twenty-three years later they were hearing them again in Stuttgart. By then they had made something like successes of their lives. They were staying at the Hotel Royal in Schloss-Strasse and, while journeying round the town, had noticed political posters with the name Hitler conspicuously displayed. They had reminded themselves of the Meldemannstrasse association but hadn't been especially interested in Hitler's progress since 1910. Nor had they been certain that it was the same Hitler; but they were soon convinced when they returned to the Royal one day and found two men in unfamiliar uniforms handing a poster to the receptionist and telling him to display it. The poster bore a picture of Hitler, who, as Chancellor, had held his first cabinet meeting on the 30th January, 1933; it was part of the campaign organized by Goering to lead up to 'The Day of the Awakening Nation'; and though Stefan and Daniel were uninterested in this or any other German political jamboree the picture confirmed that the Hitler in question was their erstwhile rival: the eyes, moustache, and forehead were unmistakable.

They had planned to stay in Stuttgart only a few days and for that reason decided to go out that evening and see more of the town. For one thing, they had a mind to look at the Wurtemberg Antiquities in the Royal Library, which they thought might be open in the evening; for another, they'd heard there was an effervescent variety performance at the Court Theatre and they had a mind to take this in as an entertaining conclusion to the day. They dressed and prepared for their excursion, but in the foyer they were stopped by a thuggish character wearing the same uniform as the bearer of the posters – brown shirt and knee-length boots.

'Departure is forbidden. Everyone is to remain indoors. Departure is forbidden until the morning.'

Naturally Stefan and Daniel were annoyed by this violation of freedom. They protested that they were visitors to Germany, produced their valid passports and visas, and became somewhat aggressive. The soldier, policeman – whatever he was – became even more aggressive.

'Forbidden,' he said again, and put his hand on the gun in his belt. He added something about Communist scum and larded his remark over with a sneering suggestion that as departure was forbidden Stefan and Daniel might just as well go to bed early. 'You will be more comfortable in bed than in the hands of the police.'

At that moment they were approached and addressed by another resident of the hotel – unmistakably an Englishman, mid-forties, slender, fair, well but casually dressed in flannel slacks, fair-isle pullover and tweed coat, and with the scrubbed look of a three-baths-a-day routine.

He told them, 'I think you'd be well advised to keep the fuss to a minimum. I felt much as you do when I was kept in by these over-hospitable people. But I see we're up against a determined opposition. I don't know what's behind it all, but I don't think there's much point in arguing against nasty looks *and* guns. Unless, of course, you have to catch trains or keep life-and-death appointments – in which case a phone call to the British Consul might help.'

'There is no telephone for foreigners tonight,' the brown-shirt said.

'You see?' the Englishman said. 'It's baffling but very definite. I know just how you feel. I've passed the stage of seething indignation personally, but I certainly went through it. I'm resigned now and I suggest you join me in my room, where we can have a bottle of wine and something to eat and discuss the mysterious ways of the authorities.'

This they did. All the residents' rooms by now had had the window shutters closed and locked from the outside, but as the

shutters were of the slatted kind it was still possible to get a re-
stricted view of the street below. The view was of a street that
was at first completely deserted; later, however, companies of
men in the now familiar uniform began to march through the
town. Although in military formations their footsteps were
curiously muffled. They sounded like a continuous subdued
drum roll, and in the faint street lighting they had a ghostly and
sinister appearance. No guns, wagons, or horses accompanied
them, and this overt lack of military trappings frighteningly
suggested a covert strength impossible to engage. The brown
companies passed, with no more than the punctuation of spaces
dividing them, for several hours. Many thousands of men must
have passed through Stuttgart that night – whence, whither, or
with what object none of the three men in the hotel room knew.
They speculated, but all they felt sure about was that Hitler was
the mysterious power behind some military-political manoeuvre.
This led Stefan and Daniel to say that they had known him in
Vienna; but for the moment they said no more than that: one
does not reveal humiliating facts about one's past life to comparative strangers. And in any case the Englishman knew
nothing of German politics and had not been aware of Hitler's
existence until that day, so was not curious about his companions'
previous association with a vague neo-political figure.

But later, when the town was once more silent, the three men
opened another bottle of wine and got around to more personal
conversation. Stefan and Daniel spoke of their business and their
plans for travel and then asked the Englishman what his line
was.

'I'm a doctor,' he told them. 'I'm on a short vacation at the
moment, getting myself fitted up for a pretty arduous year at
my hospital in England.'

They were interested, as people invariably are in doctors and
illness. 'Any special sort of doctor?' they wanted to know. He
told them yes, he was in fact a venereologist; but he told them in
the tone of a man who expects to close the conversation by his
statement – an experience he was familiar with and slightly

amused by but never avoided if led into it. He fully understood that people breaking up the conversational ice-floes with their sharp little teeth preferred illness to have glamorous or senti-mental, rather than squalid, overtones.

In this case, however, Stefan and Daniel responded with considerable interest and, since the conversation went on well into the small hours, eventually revealed that they themselves had been victims of syphilitic infection. 'Only today,' they added, 'we caught sight of Hitler's name on all these posters and realized that he was the chap we'd shared everything with – including the girl and the syphilis – in those old days in Vienna. I wonder if he went as long as we did without treatment – or indeed with-out knowing that we'd got the thing?'

'It's possible he was never treated at all,' the Doctor said. 'In nineteen-ten there wasn't much effective treatment to be had. And there's still a theory – personally I strongly disagree with it – that no treatment at all is the best treatment. My own experience is that untreated, or ineffectively treated, syphilis leads to disaster – for the infected person and a good many other people.'

Though he was only making agreeable conversation on a topic of common interest with a couple of agreeable strangers fortui-tously met, and couldn't have realized the significance of his remark, the Doctor had made a prophecy. It might also have been called the under-statement of the year. The disaster to which Hitler's syphilis led was the Second World War.

# 3   A Majestic Enmity

One of the better arrangements in the world is that disasters are
seldom unmitigated by benefits. Beethoven was a congenital
syphilitic – pock-marked, irascible, constantly troubled by
internal pains, and increasingly deaf from the age of thirty.
Many people would say that his deafness and early death (he
was fifty-seven) were disasters of the greatest magnitude to
music. But so far as his deafness is concerned this isn't necessarily
so. The syphilitic manifestation that in Hitler's case turned out
to be megalomania can be characterized by a creative as well as
a destructive aspect. As anyone who has had anything to do with
afflicted people knows, nature observes rigid laws of compensa-
tion. The blind develop remarkable powers of touch, smell, hearing; the deaf are peculiarly adapted to non-aural sensations; the
limbless accomplish astonishing feats with a pen or brush held
in the mouth. Syphilis that attacks the brain or any of the cranial
nerves is often met by a counter-attack in the form of a development of the faculties of judgment and creation; and the result is
supra-normal creative ability instead of megalomania, though it
may carry undertones of megalomania with it, as it did with
Beethoven. Just as often, the destruction by syphilis of the brain
or parts of the nervous system results in a diminution of natural
creative talent. Benvenuto Cellini is an example of the artists to
whom this happened. If the larger part of a person's natural
talent is in the field of administration or kingship instead of art
it can dwindle away into hopeless muddle-headedness and crazy
errors of judgment, as with Philip II of Spain, or turn
into maniacal cruelty as with Ivan the Terrible and Mary Tudor,
or wretched imbecility as with Henry VIII. Sometimes the
creative ability is almost the last spark to glow in a body syphi-

litically corrupted into a state of wasting, paralysis, and blindness, as with Delius.

A greatly simplified version of the medical explanation for this deviation from the normal in individuals afflicted with destructive diseases like syphilis is this: the ordinary healthy human body is a balanced arrangement of cells assembled in various forms that we call blood, veins, organs, tissues, nerves, bones, and so on; if any of these cells are permanently destroyed, the tendency is for some of the others to grow bigger or more numerous in an attempt to restore the balance. In the case of Beethoven the cells forming and controlling the creative faculties were the ones that attempted the restoring; in the case of Ivan, it was those forming and controlling the nerves that vent emotional anger and cruelty that multiplied or enlarged themselves. With Cellini and Philip II the restoration of balance apparently failed. Why one set of cells rather than another should rush into the breach is not altogether accountable. But it seems reasonable to assume that the characteristics or faculties that are already highly developed because of an increase in the size or number of cells controlling them due to heredity or environment, are the ones most likely to be affected when any restoration of balance becomes necessary. To exemplify Beethoven again: he was a musical child, having inherited the talent from his father, but his early works are for the most part tinkling imitations of Haydn and certainly don't display any signs of genius (they occasionally reveal an individual voice, though, as in the piano sonata in C minor, opus 13). Nor do any of his works up to the time of the eighth symphony (1812, when he was forty-two), though the individual voice had by then become stronger, and his music undoubtedly towered higher than that of his contemporaries. After the ravages of syphilis had made him completely deaf, however, his music shows the unmistakable quality of genius. The Mass, the ninth symphony, the last six piano sonatas, the Diabelli variations, the last quartets, are works of supra-normal creative ability. The difference between excellence and genius exemplified in music is a matter for specialized

explanation and I shall not start any arguments I can't finish.
But ask any music critic. None of them will deny that much of
Beethoven's music composed before 1812 is great in the sense of
being organically remarkable and aurally original; but they
won't deny either that the works of the last seven years of his life
are on a very much higher plane than 'great'. They are the
works of a genius. And by my reckoning Beethoven achieved this
supra-normal condition because he was a syphilitic. Other
people have been born with an arrangement of cells that ensured
their genius without the assistance of syphilis (Homer, Alexander
the Great, Shakespeare, Mozart, and Newton, for example);
and millions have died miserably of the disease without making
so much as a single visible scratch on the surface of history. But
history can do no more than record the visible scratches. Only
in its most imaginative moments does it concern itself with the
people who have apparently scratched nothing. No musical
historian that I can discover has yet gone into the problem of
why one (or possibly both) of Beethoven's parents had syphilis.
His father was a minor court musician addicted to booze, his
mother was the daughter of a cook and when she married the
elder Beethoven he was scarred about the face in a typically
syphilitic manner. But was he, too, congenitally afflicted by the
disease, or did he contract it by way of some tumble in the hay
with a Bonn whore? If so, where did *she* get it from? The ninth
symphony exists without doubt; it is visible and audible and its
creator is recorded in history, having made his mark; but its true
clinical genealogy is not noted anywhere.

Similarly, the lineage of Britain's monarchy was changed by
Mary Tudor's barrenness, which was caused by the syphilis inherited from her father Henry VIII. But even if she'd been
fertile it seems improbable that the children born to her of her
marriage to Philip of Spain would have been anything but
weakly or idiotic – as were the children of Philip's three other
marriages, for he was as riddled with syphilis as was Henry
VIII. The whole course of the Reformation, too, would surely
have been changed if Mary's syphilitic cruelty had not led her

to burn heretics by the hundred at the stake. Yet who knows which of Henry's lusty fornications infected him, or how his partner in that history-changing enterprise was herself infected, or whether it was, as is popularly supposed, Cardinal Wolsey who infected him by whispering in his ear? . . . And so on, back into the mists of venereal succession.

The courses of philosophy, literature, and painting have likewise been changed by syphilis and the other venereal diseases, sometimes disastrously, sometimes not (so far as anyone can establish what is ultimately good or bad in these spheres of activity).

Nietzsche's later works, which extolled the doctrine of Superman to megalomanic heights and consigned to bitter hells every altruistic and humanitarian quality of Christianity, were the result of his progress toward General Paralysis of the Insane, of which he died in 1900. I cannot trace the origin of his syphilis, except to an unsubstantiated comment that he caught it while a student at Leipzig. His biographers (his sister, Frau Förster-Nietzsche, and Daniel Halévy) show the customary euphemistic attitude toward his thirty years of illness and would have everybody believe that it was caused by dysentery contracted in the Franco-Prussian war of 1870, when he was in the ambulance service. But the severity of the symptoms they describe far exceeds those of such a simple malady: he had violent neuralgia, insomnia, eye weakness, stomach ills, jaundice, eventual blindness, and insanity accompanied by delusions of egotistical grandeur – extraordinary consequences of dysentery but all unmistakable symptoms of syphilis. He was apparently no womanizer (though that of course doesn't preclude the possibility of his sexual association with women on one or more occasions) and I am inclined to think that he caught his syphilis in the humanitarian pursuit of healing (an irony he would not have appreciated in his last crazy years). He was attending a cartload of German wounded during a nightmare journey from France to Carlsruhe – a journey of three days and nights made in bitter cold and torrential rain; the wounded were described by his biographers as having 'dysentery and diphtheria', but the manifestations of their illness were purulent sores and open ulcers which Nietzche continually bathed and dressed, using rainwater and boracic ointment. Neither dysentery nor diphtheria is characterized by sores, but syphilis certainly is – and the sores are highly infectious. A few weeks later Nietzsche himself had sores and was in turn nursed in gratitude by one of the soldiers he had attended during the nightmare journey. The sores disappeared, as is characteristic of the syphilitic variety, and Nietzsche thought he had recovered. He never did recover. The doctors he went to appear to have been mystified, but probably they were ignorant or viewed his illness with typically Victorian horror. They merely prescribed rest and 'cures' at various watering places. He attempted to deaden the miseries of the later stages with chloral, but this only fed additional poison into his body. His natural affinity with the idea of 'the forceful ego' gradually developed into insane megalomania as the reasoning powers of his brain rotted away under the attack of syphilis on the cells controlling them. And this was the man whose mad philosophy of the worship of force was seized on by Hitler when he too was consumed by the same disease. So the souring up of Nietzsche's philosophy by syphilis is an effect that the whole world has had to cope with; and it may still have to be reckoned with in the future.

A Hungarian doctor named János Plesch has gone at some length in his book *Rembrandt im Rembrandt* into the possibility that Rembrandt was syphilitic. He bases his suggestion mainly on the notion that in many of the famous paintings there are hidden fantasy subjects which may be discerned by looking 'with half-closed eyes' from 'a certain distance' (much as one can make out emergent patterns in wallpaper designs, cloud formations, or lumps of coal in a fire), and that these fantasy subjects are a product of Rembrandt's syphilitically disordered mind. His notion is to me incomprehensible, since I can see nothing but the obvious subjects of the pictures in spite of a good deal of diagramming and arrows pointing to supposed 'mystically

veiled' figures. However, it's an idea. Rembrandt may have been
syphilitic (his son Titus certainly was); and if so his syphilis may
have affected the quality of his painting. But there was another
painter, Paul Gauguin, who was certainly syphilitic, whose painting was influenced by the disease, and who consequently influenced later painters to a considerable extent.

Gauguin, you remember, was the man who abandoned his
respectable Danish wife and children and went to live in Tahiti.
Syphilis is rife there and no doubt Gauguin would have caught
it sooner or later; but in fact he became infected in Denmark
during his career in the navy as a young man. He wasn't treated
until near the end of his life, when it was far too late and he
had attempted suicide while in a state of acute pain and melancholia. But from his letters one can tell that his artistic vision
was most strongly influenced by the heightened perception that
in his case was brought on by continual pain. Like Beethoven, he
had a natural and highly developed individual talent for his
art; but it was a talent that burgeoned into genius (with such
masterpieces as 'Nevermore' and 'The Gold of Their Bodies')
only after the attacks of syphilis on his nervous system had been
compensated for by the development of that part of it that controlled his inner vision. And all the graphic arts since his death
in 1903 have been touched in some degree by that vision.

In literature, Charles Baudelaire was one writer whose works
have had an incisive effect on his successors. His poems' concern
with the erotic, their spiritual significance, and their rejection of
cant and sentimentality are characteristics that are easily dis-
cernible in literature from the time of Dorothy M. Richardson
onward and may be seen through the mists of literary development that followed Baudelaire's death in 1867 and cleared about
the end of the century. If these characteristics derive largely
from Baudelaire it is only because in the first place he
deliberately infected himself with syphilis in pursuit of the depth
of experience that would allow him, a man of fastidious temperament and refined mind, to know squalor, disease, heterosexual and homosexual lust, and depths of depravity that he

might not otherwise have known subjectively. He tried hashish and opium to extend his experience – and to help subdue the acute melancholia brought on by syphilis, and he wrote his later works from the depths of despair and the paralytic insanity that was to kill him at the age of forty-six. But he extended the bounds of literature by his sacrifice; and it seems extremely doubtful whether, for example, Henry Miller's *Tropic of Cancer* or William Burroughs' *The Naked Lunch* would exist as they do exist today without the expensive experiment made by Baudelaire.

Another great literary disaster of modern times was the sexual, and later the mental, derangement of Oscar Wilde. Jointly these deviations were responsible for two of the saddest trials at law in British history and for the cessation of a brilliant talent. Both were due to syphilis. Mr H. Montgomery Hyde says in *The Trials of Oscar Wilde* : 'Certain it is that Wilde betrayed no signs of abnormality in adolescence and early manhood. On the contrary, his inclinations seem to have been decidedly heterosexual. While an undergraduate at Oxford, he contracted syphilis as the result of a casual connexion, probably with a prostitute. In those days the recognized treatment for this disease was with mercury. In Wilde's case this treatment undoubtedly produced the discolouration and decay of his teeth, which remained a permanent feature of his appearance for the remainder of his life and added to the general impression of physical overgrowth and ugliness which his person presented on acquaintance. Nor, it may be added, was there the slightest suggestion of effeminacy about him, either at Oxford or at any subsequent period . . . We know, too, that he was deeply in love with his wife at the time of their marriage, and that they experienced normal sexual intercourse. Indeed, two sons were born of the union before the rift between them took place . . . Before proposing to his wife, Wilde had been to consult a doctor in London, who had assured him that he was completely cured of his youthful malady. On the strength of his assurance he got married. About two years later he discovered to his dismay that all traces of syphilis had not been eradicated from his system, and it was this unpleasant discovery which obliged him to discontinue physical relations with his wife. In the result, *inter alia*, he turned toward homosexuality. The trials that ensued were, as everyone knows, disastrous for Wilde; equally so were the ravages of the disease (which can be traced in *The Picture of Dorian Gray* and several other works that deal with the corruption of the flesh), for his creative mind ceased to function after he left prison and went to France.' Although it would not be true in Wilde's case to say that his influential works were affected by his disease (the 'corruptive' pieces like *Dorian Gray* and some of the fairy tales have had scarcely any literary influence in the sense that Baudelaire's *Fleurs du Mal* had), it is certainly true that the repercussions caused by his trials were widely felt in both the literary and social worlds, which have never quite recovered from them. The name of Wilde can rarely be mentioned without implications – whether or not intended – of homosexuality. And for a reason that you now have seen – though other commentators and biographers than Mr Montgomery Hyde have hedged round the subject in the customary euphemistic way. It is surprising how many serious biographers of famous people either ignore or are mealy-mouthed about the effects of syphilis on their subjects and consequently on history. This is understandable in the case of biographies of people whose immediate relatives are still alive and might be hurt by the truth; but there seems little point in muffling the word 'syphilis' in such flannel as 'incurable disease' and 'loathsome disease' or falsely describing the malady as 'cancer' or 'overwork' when writing about such very dead syphilitics as Schumann, Schubert, Christian VII of Denmark, Strindberg, Swift, De Maupassant, Hugo Wolf, Endre Ady, Henry VIII, Manet, Schopenhauer, Paganini, and Napoleon. Yet one continually encounters biographers who delicately (or ignorantly) skate round what was the most important clinical fact in their subjects' lives. The effect is misleading to say the least.

In the case of Napoleon, innumerable words have suggested

that he was murdered, that he died of cancer, that he had incurable hepatitis, that he committed suicide. But the three
doctors who attended him on St Helena (Dr O'Meara, Dr
Stockoe, and Dr Antommarchi) all prescribed mercury, the
standard treatment for syphilis in those days; and Napoleon
himself told Dr Stockoe that he had been infected with syphilis
before the Italian and Egyptian campaigns of 1796–1798. It
attacked his stomach and liver and, as Dr Henry, one of the
surgeons at the autopsy noted, also resulted 'in complete atrophy
of the genital organs'. It was only natural that 'recurrent hepatitis due to lack of exercise and the unhealthy climate of St
Helena' and 'hereditary cancer of the stomach' should be given
as the causes of his death : they are diseases more befitting a hero
than the dreadful plague which his own wars helped to spread.
The implacable enmity of such a disease, with its ability to
change the course of the world's history is, in its way, of some
majesty. It is an enmity worthy of dissection and analysis by a
good doctor.

# 4   A Consultation

These, then, are the protagonist and antagonist of this story : a
doctor and a disease. And a disease, moreover, that manifested
itself in another enemy, a man with an infamous name, far better
known than the small organism to which he played host for so
long. But Hitler's enmity was only temporary. The disease has
so far remained stubbornly permanent.

By 'disease' I mean in fact a number of maladies known collectively as venereal diseases. 'Venereal' is of course derived
through *venereus* from *Venus*, who was the Roman goddess of
love, and the word means, somewhat imprecisely, love, lust,
sexual desire, and, when qualifying 'disease', any of several contagious maladies that are acquired typically during copulation –
and these include such extremes as syphilis in humans and
cloacitis in fowls.

I have already explained in my foreword that by 'doctor' I
mean a particular doctor with a name, a home, a consulting
room, a number of degrees earned by hard work and brilliance,
and patients to take care of.

The Doctor and the smaller enemy, Hitler, were contemporaries. 'You might say we were students together,' the Doctor
said to me once; 'though in somewhat different circumstances.
But we weren't always geographically far apart. During the time
Hitler was kicking around Linz and Vienna with Kubizek and
Stefan and Daniel I was a student at Heidelburg. I hadn't
decided on medicine as a career then. My father, who was a
country solicitor with a private income as well as his professional
one, sent me abroad to pick up languages and study generally.
That was quite a conventional thing to do in those days. I don't

know who said "travel broadens the mind", but that was the
general idea. You didn't need passports or any of that nonsense.
A British five-pound note would get you out of almost any difficulty. People weren't suspicious of each other at an international
level as they are today – not ordinary people, anyway; maybe
it was different if you were in politics or the diplomatic service.
You learnt Latin and French and German – and in my case
Greek – and when you'd got a grounding in these languages you
went to France and Germany to see the people the languages
belonged to and learn the idiomatic speech. And you enjoyed
it – I did, anyway. Everyone seemed to have much more capacity
for enjoyment in those days. It wasn't a matter of monetary
values but of philosophic ones. I think we looked and listened
more – or perhaps we looked and listened more closely. There
was more interest in people for their own sakes.'

The difference in the circumstances of the Doctor and Hitler
were considerable; their geographical propinquity around 1909
was coincidental. I shan't labour it. Nor shall I write more than
a biographical sketch of Hitler to point the considerable
difference in circumstances: but that much, I think, is necessary
before you can consider the Doctor's argument about his smaller
adversary in the proper light.

Hitler's father was the bastard son of a peasant, his mother
the daughter of another peasant; and the two were second
cousins. Alois Hitler, the father, began life as a shoemaker but
had delusions of grandeur which he satisfied at the age of forty
by becoming a minor customs official. On the way to this station
in life he acquired three wives, the third being Klara Poelzl,
aged seventeen at the time of her marriage to Alois in 1885 and
already pregnant by him. The child of this pregnancy, a son
called Gustav, lived only two years. Two later children also died
before Adolf was born on 20th April, 1889, and another son,
Edmund, born in 1894, died in 1900. The youngest child,
Adolf's sister Paula, was born in 1896 and lived – outlived Adolf
in fact.

Alois Hitler changed his name from Schicklgruber (his mother's name) to Hitler (his father's) in 1876 so that he could legally become the beneficiary of a will; and Alois's father changed his name from Hiedler to Hitler for no discoverable reason. I've seen it suggested that he changed it because he was a staunch Catholic and the name of Hiedler had Jewish connotations, but the evidence to back this suggestion is slight – no more, in fact, than that Hiedlers are common among eastern European Jewish families, which is not evidence of a particular Hiedler being Jewish. Adolf, anyway, was born and baptized into the Catholic Church at Brannau-on-the-Inn, a small town on the frontier dividing Bavaria from Austria. He seems to have had a strong filial devotion to his parents. Kubizek says passionately :

'Adolf really loved his mother. I swear to it before God and man. I remember many occasions when he showed this love for his mother most deeply and movingly during her last illness [she died of cancer in 1907]; he never spoke of his mother but with deep affection. He was a good son. It was beyond his power to fulfil her most heartfelt wish to see him started on a safe career. When we lived together in Vienna he always carried his mother's portrait with him.'

Alois too seems to have drawn his meed of affection from the subsequently unaffectionate Adolf. Alois was a Hindenbergian man to look at, pedantic and constantly indignant by nature. He was always inveighing against something, and it was during the leap between one of these states of indignation and another that he died of a coronary thrombosis on 3rd January, 1903, aged sixty-five. 'When the fourteen-year-old son saw his dead father,' Kubizek says, 'he burst out into uncontrollable weeping.'

Adolf was also affectionately inclined toward a girl called discreetly by Kubizek 'Stefanie'. In fact according to Kubizek's evidence he was her love-lorn swain. She was considerably above Hitler's social station and used to drive daily along the Linz promenade in a carriage with her mother. Hitler stood with his friends on the sidewalk and tried to ogle her. But 'from time to time the two ladies were to be seen in the company of young officers. Poor, pallid youngsters like Adolf naturally could not hope to cope with these young lieutenants in their smart uniforms . . . his anger, in the end, led him into uncompromising enmity toward the officer class as a whole, and everything military in general. "Conceited blockheads," he used to call them. It annoyed him intensely that Stefanie mixed with such idlers who, he insisted, wore corsets and used scent'. This abortive adoration (he never actually met Stefanie, though she smiled at him once) went on for four years in the characteristically sloppy way of novelettes. 'Hitler,' Kubizek continues, 'wrote countless love poems to Stefanie; "Hymn to the Beloved" was the title of one of them, which he read to me from his little black notebook: Stefanie, a high-born damsel, in a dark-blue flowing gown, rode on a white steed over the flowering meadows, her loose hair fell in golden waves on her shoulders. A clear spring sky was above. Everything was pure, radiant joy. I can still see Adolf's face glowing with fervent ecstasy and hear his voice reciting these verses. Stefanie filled his thoughts so completely that everything he said, or did, or planned for the future, was centred around her. With his growing estrangement from his home, Stefanie gained more and more influence over my friend, although he never spoke a word to her.'

Hitler's estrangement from his home was due simply to Alois's determination to make his son a civil servant and Adolf's equal determination to become a painter – which was, for him, a way of saying that he just didn't want to work. He had a minuscule talent for drawing – especially architectural drawing – and greatly inflated it in his own mind. He says in *Mein Kampf* that when he boldly told his father what he wanted to do Alois replied, 'Artist! Not as long as I live, never!' Looking at Hitler's vapid water colours, which are of about the same value to visual art that 'In a Monastery Garden' is to music, one can't help feeling that Alois's indignant discouragement was a good thing, though it was a social indignation rather than an aesthetic one.

The enstrangement became translated into terms of actual separation after Alois died – but not for several years. Hitler was too stupid and too idle to pass his school-leaving examination and his mother kept him cosseted in the home until she died in 1907. When he moved to Vienna in 1909 the object of his foray on the city was to get into the Academy of Art there. Secretly he had decided that, like Michelangelo, he was an architect rather than a painter. The Academy, however, decided without any secrecy at all that he was neither and refused him admission.

After the death of his mother he had no reason to return to Linz and the estrangement from his home town became complete. It was then that he was forced to live on such wits as he had. The same Neumann who had given him the overcoat acted as his agent for a time, accompanying him to shops and persuading the proprietors to commission posters and price-tickets which Hitler would do on the spot; and the man Hanisch who lived with him at Meldemannstrasse toted the water colours painted in more leisurely hours round picture-framers and often sold them on Hitler's behalf. (Hanisch's kindness was repaid by Hitler taking legal action against him for the alleged embezzlement of part of a sum Hanisch got for a picture; and Hanisch was sent to prison for a week, the case having been proved.) Hanisch, Stefan and Daniel, and a man called Siegfried Loffner have all confirmed that Hitler lived as they all did by beating carpets, carrying bags and getting cabs for travellers, casual labouring on building works, dish-washing in cafés, and scavenging round dustbins. He had a great distaste for regular work, preferring to earn a little money and spend it frugally in cafés where he read newspapers and harangued the customers on politics.

He was a great bore with his continual sounding-off about injustices and inefficiencies in 'the system', his spouting of half-digested information from indiscriminate reading, and his dotty ideas for acquiring riches and fame. And like most manic-depressives he was always either sullen or exuberant, shattering everyone's peace with rantings against Jews, Habsburgs, Catholics,

or Social Democrats, or withdrawing into himself and refusing
to say anything to anybody. He was a self-confessed cheat even
before he left Linz. He told Hanisch that he had many times
faked 'old masters' by painting pictures in oils and baking them
in the oven so that they turned yellow and apparently ancient.
And with considerable practice in cheap oratory he learnt to
cheat with words too, so that sloppy platitudes could be so spiced
with paranoiac bitterness that they sounded like the trumpetings
of a saviour of the German race.

Primed with this résumé of Hitler's background up to the
fatal year of 1910 I went along to the Doctor's consulting-room
in the late summer of 1963. I had already been introduced to
him by an intermediary who had heard him skim over his argument and the supporting evidence and had suggested that, as a
reporter of anything and anybody of lively interest, I might like
to report on the Doctor and his argument. The idea had
appealed to me and I had made my approach thinking there
might perhaps be a longish article for one of the intelligent
monthlies in the story. It soon became obvious that the Doctor
himself was of more than average interest, and that the disease,
the big enemy he had fought for most of his working life, had
fascinations far beyond the squalid or pornographic. I prepared
for the purdah the writer must go into if he wants to get anything worthwhile done and started researching for a book. Obviously the monthlies weren't going to be big enough spacewise
to cope with what I had to say; but a book is a conveniently
elastic repository for a garrulous reporter's findings.

So there I was in the consulting-room, clutching my résumé,
which I gave to the Doctor to read while I trained my eye on the
scene that clearly was to be the venue for a great many more
talks.

There's a feeling of immense gratitude to be gained from the
ability to be objective about a doctor and his consulting-room.
Had I gone there to discuss my own bodily ailments I could
never have viewed the man or the place with clarity. My eye

would have been misted by apprehension or self-pity, my judgment impaired by pain or fear. The furnishing of the room might have appeared monstrous, the Doctor a sinister harbinger of doom. But in a state of good health the vision is unclouded by personal jitters and the scene can be catalogued as is.

The room is large and untidy, littered with piles of *The Lancet* and the *British Medical Journal*. There's a leather sofa under the window, a couple of leather armchairs, and a reproduction of Turner's *Rain, Steam and Speed* on one wall. Bookshelves hold 473 impressive medical tomes (I counted them in idle moments while the Doctor answered the phone, which he was frequently called to do). In the middle of the room there's an adjustable bed for patients to be examined on; and in an alcove there's a sink below some shelves holding jars, bottles, surgical instruments, and a microscope.

The Doctor himself seems to have changed remarkably little since 1933, when he was snapped in the fair-isle pullover and sports coat in which he met Stefan and Daniel. His fair hair has taken on a shaking of pepper-and-salt but has thinned scarcely at all; he is still slender to the point of spareness; his teeth exhibit a few gold fillings; thick-rimmed reading glasses are tucked behind the silk handkerchief in the breast pocket; but he doesn't look especially like a doctor. He's a man who laughs a lot, rather noisily, and moves about with a curiously angular grace. He pauses quite a long while before speaking, but once started is not at all hesitant and rarely sidetracks himself.

When he had read my résumé he said, 'Yes, Hitler was, as you see, an unendearing character even in his youth. Like his father he had slight megalomania. He was unstable, an idealist who twisted his vision of the world (it was only the German world in those days) so that he could see himself in the middle of it, and a paranoiac who wanted to draw attention to the alleged persecutions of his class and race by bearing them on his own shoulders so that he could act as a martyr. All the elements of his subsequent tyranny were in fact already evident in his character when he was living, destitute, in Vienna in 1910.'

I asked the Doctor what he thought might have happened if Hitler hadn't gone to Vienna, and he said, 'It's profitless to speculate on what *might* have happened – if, for instance, his megalomania hadn't become concentrated into a virulent hatred of the Jewish race, with his additional hatreds of priests, Negroes, Social Democrats, Habsburgs, and Czechs as supporting side-issues. It's more sensible to point to the likelihood of his secret fears, his secret inferiority, being tipped sideways into active anti-Semitism by his experience with Hannah.'

I agreed that we would examine that likelihood.

'Long before Hitler got there in nineteen-nine there was a great deal of anti-Semitism prevalent in Vienna and there's no doubt that some of it brushed off on him. He was a man with a chameleonic ability to absorb other people's opinions, and anti-Semitism no doubt suited him very well. All the evidence points to the fact that he was a man of puny sexual achievement which, to avoid consciousness of his inferiority, he distorted into a deliberate austerity. Hanisch, Loffner, and Kubizek all speak of his militant contempt for alcohol and tobacco, and his awkwardness with women. His screwy devotion to Stefanie is a good example of that awkwardness. I don't believe he was impotent or an onanist : I think he was normally sexed but unable to find any woman who wanted him – which is understandable, God knows. This of course wouldn't normally have mattered : there must be millions of men who remain virgins until well into their twenties without the fact going sour on them. But the Jews are incontrovertibly a sexually virile people – a fact it was scarcely possible to ignore in the anti-Semitic propaganda that flourished in Vienna in 1910; and this, I believe, was one of the scabs of anti-Semitism that knocked off on Hitler. Years later he wrote something in *Mein Kampf* that gives the clue. If you've got the book there, as I see you have, we can look it up.'

The passage proved to be easily found and read : 'The nightmare vision of the seduction of hundreds of thousands of girls by repulsive, crooked-legged Jew bastards . . . The black-haired Jewish youth lies in wait for hours on end, satanically glaring at and spying on the unsuspicious girl whom he plans to seduce, adulterating her blood and removing her from the bosom of her own people.'

'I can easily imagine,' the Doctor went on, 'his Judaeophobia taking shape in the raving jealousy that inspired that piffle. For self-assurance's sake he would need to demonstrate that he too could "seduce . . . adulterate" – whatever his phrase was – and who better to seduce and adulterate than a Jewish whore, so that humiliation of her race could be combined with proof of his virility?'

'I see,' I said. 'And then he gets infected with her syphilis and this is the deciding factor. It's what canalizes an ordinary chip-on-the-shoulder bitterness into a vicious concentrated hatred?'

'Exactly. But there's a danger in over-simplification. It wouldn't have happened for years. As you'll see when we come to discuss the disease, the symptoms are unpredictably variable, visible symptoms such as sores – which are painless – come and go, leaving no sign; the non-irritating rash Stefan and Daniel mentioned is present in only about forty per cent of cases; a feeling of ill-being is often vague and transitory. The general tendency in untreated syphilis is invariably for the subject to suppose that the illness – whatever it may have been – has passed with the visible signs, which, even without treatment, gradually disappear. And even if Hitler had known earlier than I believe he knew, the available treatment in nineteen-ten was just as crude as it had been for about seven hundred years. At the end of that year, true, Salvarsan – "Six-o-Six" as it's called – was introduced, but it was very much of a medical novelty and certainly wouldn't have been available to anyone in Hitler's position. My own view is that he had syphilis for many years before it was really adequately treated; and when, after he came to power, his condition was examined properly, it was too late to prevent the damage which had already devastated his tissues – particularly those of his nervous system. Daniel and Stefan told me, as I've just said, that although their own treatment was somewhat delayed, in their case the treatment, when they had it, was effective. As I must emphasize again, individuals' resistance varies enormously. In the case of these three men who were all infected from the same source, Stefan and Daniel overcame the infection – and they certainly did, because they're alive and well today – and Hitler didn't. You'll see more readily how that could easily happen when you do some research on the disease. But broadly speaking it was because the organism that's the cause of all the trouble, a germ called *Spirochaeta pallida,* attacked in a different way in the case of Hitler, and because his natural resistance against that particular attack was poor. Possibly, also, because the treatment he had in the early days – if and when he had it – was inadequate.'

The Doctor paused, backtracking to the object of his dissertation. 'Oh yes. I was explaining all this to back up my contention that Hitler's virulent hatred of Jews – as distinct from the mere unreasoning dislike of them that he absorbed from the Viennese political climate of the time – was slow to develop. All that vitriolic stuff in *Mein Kampf* was written in 1924 when he was a political prisoner of the Munich People's Court, incarcerated in a fortress at Landsberg. And by that time *Spirochaeta pallida* had had a good chance to get to work on his brain, especially that part of it where the faculties of judgment lie. And my view is that his mentality, already tending to megalomania and instability and affected now by the certain knowledge that he had syphilis, would naturally seek an outlet of vicious revenge. And it wouldn't be enough for such a revenge to be aimed at the single member of Jewish society who had infected him : the entire race had to be persecuted in castigation.'

I absorbed this elaboration of the Doctor's argument for a while. It was an agreeable feature of my talks with him that at mid-afternoon his secretary would bring in two cups of tea and a plate of digestive biscuits, and I let this innocent refreshment sink in with the argument before I asked : 'What evidence is there that Hitler knew he had syphilis when he was writing *Mein Kampf* in nineteen-twenty-four ?'

'I don't know, but there are several strong indications. Stefan and Daniel both knew that Hitler as well as themselves had contracted it from the same girl, and all three of them must have known it within six months after the infection. Also, all the books – including *Mein Kampf* – mention that he was gassed in a British attack on the French village of Comines on the evening of the thirteenth of October, nineteen-eighteen, and that he was temporarily blinded as a result. But this isn't altogether so. A specialist friend of mine had some conversation with the German eye specialist who treated Hitler. His name was Krückmann, and he told my friend that what he treated Hitler for was a fortnight's *hysterical* blindness – a very different thing from gas blindness, and a possible symptom of syphilis. Now what I think happened was that Hitler was sent back from the front to a hospital in Pomerania to have treatment for his eyes, Krückmann diagnosed his trouble as hysterical blindness, and passed him on for further diagnosis. It was then that he was discovered to be suffering from syphilis and given some rough and ready treatment, but in eight years, in his particular case, the disease had gained too strong a hold to be easily shifted and it went on attacking him for the rest of his life.'

I should interpolate here, I think, that the Doctor's argument is supported by evidence from another source – the memoirs of Felix Kersten, who was personal doctor to Heinrich Himmler, chief of the Gestapo. (Kersten was a therapist who was able to relieve Himmler of pain caused by an internal illness and thereby to gain his complete confidence. During many of his healing sessions with Himmler he convinced the police chief of the advisability of releasing thousands of political prisoners who might otherwise have gone to their deaths by torture or the gas chamber, and what might be called his slow blackmail of Himmler was of incalculable benefit to humanity.) Kersten writes in his diary for 12th December, 1942 :

'This was the most exciting day I've had since I first began treating Himmler. He was very nervous and restless; I realized that he had something on his mind and questioned him about it. His reply was to ask me: "Can you treat a man suffering from severe headaches, dizziness and insomnia?"

' "Of course, but I must examine him before I can give a definite opinion", I answered. "Above all I must know the cause of these symptoms."

'Himmler replied: "I'll tell you who he is. But you must swear to tell nobody about it and treat what I confide to you with the utmost secrecy."

'My answer was that, as a doctor, I was constantly having secrets entrusted to me; it was no new experience for me, as the strictest discretion was part of my professional duty.

'Himmler then fetched a black portfolio from his safe and took a blue manuscript from it, saying: "Read this. Here are the secret documents with the report on the Führer's illness."

'The report comprised twenty-six pages and at a first glance I realized that it had drawn freely on Hitler's medical record from the days when he lay blinded in a hospital at Pasewalk. From there the report went on to establish that in his youth as a soldier Hitler had fallen a victim to poison gas; he had been incompetently treated so that for a time he was in danger of blindness. There were also certain of the symptoms associated with syphilis. He was released from Pasewalk apparently cured. In 1937 symptoms appeared which proved that syphilis was evidently continuing its ravages; and at the beginning of 1942 symptoms of a similar nature showed beyond any shadow of doubt that Hitler was suffering from progressive paralysis. Every symptom was present except for fixity of vision and confusion of speech.

'I handed the report back to Himmler and informed him that unfortunately I could do nothing in this case, as my speciality was manual therapy, not mental disease. Himmler enquired my opinion about what should be done in such a case. I replied by asking whether Hitler was receiving treatment. "Certainly," Himmler answered. "Morell [Hitler's personal physician] is giving him injections, which he asserts will check the progress of the disease, and in any event maintain the Führer's ability to work." '

The Führer, as we know, worked like mad to conquer his human enemies for nearly three more years. But his real enemy, *Spirochaeta pallida,* was never conquered. According to the reliable evidence of Heinz Linge, his valet, he shot himself at 3.50 p.m. on 30th April, 1945. His last recorded words were all directed against Jews: 'The Jew-ridden Roosevelt . . . Churchill, this Jew-ridden, half-American drunkard . . . Jews, Russian Bolshevists and the pack of jackals that follows . . . the deadly poison of Jewry'. His lunatic ravings had reached the stage of complete mania some time before, and Linge testifies that he suffered from a palsy of the left hand and leg, acute hypochondria, continual itching of the skin, insomnia, and pains in the head and stomach. He was receiving continual injections, and in one lucid moment asked for his brain to be examined.

All these symptoms are typical of syphilis in an advanced stage, and it seems likely that if Hitler hadn't shot himself he would shortly have died from its ravages. 'Those final ravings,' the Doctor said, 'suggest that the cortex, as well as the base, of his brain was being attacked. And when the cortex is attacked General Paralysis of the Insane is the inevitable result. He was due for death anyway, but in a moment of clarity he would realize that a Führer under restraint in a madhouse hardly accorded with his vision of himself as God of the German people. Suicide was the only other way out and appeared to have more shreds of dignity about it. So there you are : another triumph for *Spirochaeta pallida,* my permanent enemy.'

He smiled, twirled round in his chair, and rang for his secretary to come and collect the tray.

'Of course it's impossible to prove that *Spirochaeta* was the direct cause of the war, but it was undoubtedly one of the causes of the way in which it was conducted. We all know about the causes of the war as revealed by the historians – the political build-up, the Germans' resentment of Versailles, the League of Nations and so on. Nobody can say what would have happened

if Hitler hadn't been there or what would have happened if he
hadn't been infected with the very organism most likely to
derange completely his already unstable psychology; but I do
most firmly believe that, given the climate in which a war could
be stirred up, it could have been brought to boiling point by a
man of Hitler's basic nature *only* because of some fortuitous
influence. That influence was syphilis. No doubt he was a crackpot in his youth; but he was an idle and pusillanimous crackpot,
and it was only derangement of his judgment caused by the
disease attacking the brain that turned him into the lunatic he
became. He was born a nonentity and he would have stayed one
but for that.'

The Doctor paused, delved for his reading glasses, polished
them over with the silk handkerchief, and went to the filing
cabinet. 'I've just remembered something Randolph Churchill
said somewhere. I've got it written down, I think.' He foraged
about among notebooks and press clippings and eventually came
up with a neatly-written note on the back of a brochure
describing Oberammagau. 'Hitler's power to change the course
of history and impose his will,' it said, 'may well be judged to
rank with that of Caesar, Napoleon and Lenin. But while the
world can understand the genius and superior mental talents
which enabled these three earlier conquerors and actual or
would-be cosmocrats to rise from obscurity to power, no one has
yet probed the dark secret of Hitler's daemon.' He took it and
replaced it, locking the drawer as he always did with a key on a
gold chain that spanned his waistcoat. 'Well, we know now what
the dark secret of his daemon was.'

'Thanks to that chance meeting with Stefan and Daniel,' I
said.

'Thanks to that so far as proof is concerned. But even without
that I think I should have had a pretty shrewd idea. When all
the pogroms were going on in the 'thirties, and while he was
surging through Europe and making those mad speeches of conquest there were plain indications of cerebral syphilis. Megalomaniac syphilitics always bash on ahead against every kind of

opposition; they even go to the extent of killing themselves –
which is of course exactly what Hitler did. And some of the
pictures of him published during that time when he was
trampling on everybody were definitely indicative. An expert
can tell by various signs – especially the eyes – when a person is
syphilitic; and although those pictures were rarely large or clear
enough to be sure, it often occurred to me that there was confirmation of Stefan and Daniel's story in some of them. Yes, that
was his daemon all right.'

I pondered this for a few minutes, then came up with a question that seemed to me of some importance.

'Did you ever pass your knowledge on to anyone in authority
– the Prime Minister, or MI5 for instance? It seems to me they
could have used it.'

'Yes. That's a good question. And indeed it did cross my mind
at the beginning of the war. But I didn't – and for three reasons.
I couldn't believe that they didn't already know – what, after
all, is an Intelligence Service for? Also, I wasn't certain whom
to approach, and I was extremely busy with my hospital work
and thought it much better to get on with my own job and let
the Government get on with theirs. But after the war was over I
met one of the big-wigs in Intelligence and asked him if it had
ever been known about Hitler's syphilis. He told me it never had.
I was horrified. I don't say it would have been possible to stop
him once the war had started; but I do say that, with expert
advice, it would have been possible to anticipate his moves. A
venereologist in cahoots with a military strategist may sound a
queer partnership, but I'll bet it would have had considerable
success. After all, a great deal of doctoring is Intelligence work
– collecting and collating information, discovering things, putting two and two together; and military strategy is very largely
being able to tell what the other side's going to do next. So there
you are – something could have been done and never was.'

This seemed to me to be somewhat arguable on the face of it.
'Granted,' I said, 'that our diplomats and politicians might have
been able to do something to prevent Hitler's war-mongering if

they'd known the cause of it as early as you did – as soon as he'd reached that position of power as Chancellor in nineteen-thirty-three in fact – isn't it likely that by that time Germany's war machine would have gathered too much impetus? Wouldn't it have rumbled on even without Hitler's leadership? And even if we'd known, could we have acted in any practical way? It doesn't seem feasible to me that Hitler could have been arrested and put away by any anti-German power simply because it was known that he was a syphilitic who by then was over the border of madness.'

The Doctor said dryly : 'I think you're trying to over-simplify the situation. Of course it wouldn't have been simple at all. But to answer your first question first : Hitler's war-mongering had scarcely started in nineteen-thirty-three. I think it's probable that Germany's war machine would have lacked any impetus at all without Hitler's leadership. He was just the man for them. Whether or not he actually understood the national psychology, he *acted* as if he did. The methods of his growing megalomania were the methods that pleased them. I doubt if anyone else would have had the same effect. I think it's much more likely that the Nazi party would have crumbled without Hitler's ceaseless jingoism to hold it together. But naturally I can't prove it – you can't prove a negative. As for your other question, I agree of course that Hitler could never have been arrested and held in captivity because some venereologist prophesied inevitable lunacy. But there are more subtle ways of doing things than that. For instance, we could have advertised the fact all over Germany that Hitler was a syphilitic and a lunatic. A fine effect that would have had on the German people! Then look at the way Felix Kersten virtually blackmailed Himmler into releasing thousands of political prisoners by being able to relieve him of pain. It was certainly known that Hitler, in the very early stages of his power, suffered from stomach disorders, headaches and insomnia, and was always seeking the doctor who could cure him. He had a man called Conti as his physician in those days. Conti was a breezy chap who advised Hitler to eat what he liked and not worry, and that wasn't the sort of treatment Hitler liked. He got rid of Conti and tried doctor after doctor until nineteen-thirty-six, when his photographer – who was himself a syphilitic – introduced him to a fashionable Berlin doctor who called himself a venereologist; but he was in fact something of a quack. However, he gave Hitler medicine which relieved his stomach pains, and this of course got him on Hitler's right side. He may have been let into the secret of Hitler's syphilis or he may have diagnosed it himself. Either way he thereafter had a hold over Hitler, who knew that he knew his guilty secret but also knew that he would at least treat him for the disease. The treatment seems to have been of the hit-or-miss variety and certainly wasn't approved of by other doctors who were called in from time to time; but they only had to disagree with Hitler's pet to be dismissed – or worse. Brandt, who was Hitler's surgeon for twelve years, was condemned to death after disagreeing with him. But my point is, supposing this quack had been an anti-Nazi doctor put in by British Intelligence? There's no knowing what he might have done to stop Hitler's antics. He might have cured him, killed him, blackmailed him as Kersten blackmailed Himmler – any number of possibilities occur. You see?'

I did see. I also saw that, for the time being, I knew as much as I cared to know about Hitler and his shenanigans. The shenanigans of *Spirochaeta pallida* seemed to me to be worth some attention, since he – or it – is the greater enemy, and hasn't as yet been brought to extinction.

# PART TWO

# The Greater Enemy

# 5   *The Marvellous Organism*

Speaking poetically, love is the oldest illness known to mankind. Man himself is a mere upstart juvenile in the evolution of the world – half a million years in a fiery, icy, rumbling geology of five thousand million years, give or take a few million. His civilization is even more youthful – a trifling five thousand years. But for all those five thousand years the more poetical of his representatives have been speaking of love as a sickness. 'Love is a sickness full of woes, all remedies refusing,' Samuel Daniel sighed in the sixteenth century, and he was only echoing the earlier sighs of countless other poets who'd arrived at the same conclusion in the civilizations of 2000 B.C.

Speaking clinically, the sicknesses of love, the venereal maladies, are probably as old as the poets' sighs. The evidence for their being that old is sparse, but I shall go into it later and present the historical frame. It seems more sensible first to have a picture to put in it.

The picture is of three principal diseases, all unpleasantly named: Chancroid, Gonorrhoea, and Syphilis. All three – and one or two others – are venereal diseases, but the etymological implication that they are all transmitted only by that manifestaion of love and lust, copulation, is clinically inaccurate: there are epidemic forms of gonorrhoea that can be transmitted by contaminated fomites in girls' schools, hereditary forms of syphilis transmissible to a child in the womb, and a great many other ways in which all the diseases may be transmitted by contact without copulation. The clinical version of love's sickness, in fact, can be quite independent of love – an irony the poets seem to have missed.

Armed with the gleanings of some heavy and somewhat

queasy reading on the venereal diseases, I sat myself on the Doctor's sofa again and heard my twisted and inadequate comprehensions sorted out with fine clarity.

'We'll take them in alphabetical order,' he said, 'and that's roughly the inverse order of importance.

'Chancroid first. The name is a synonym for soft chancre, and a chancre is, as I expect you know, a sore or ulcer that occurs at the site where an infecting organism takes its first bite, so to speak. The word will crop up a lot when we're discussing syphilis. But chancroid, the disease, is quite different from syphilis. It's caused by another organism – not *Spirochaeta pallida* at all but a tiny rod-shaped bacillus called *Haemophilus ducrevi* or *Ducrey's bacillus* because Ducrey discovered it. This bug gets into the tissues through any minute abrasion on the skin at the point of contact, or through the minute cracks between the cells of the skin as it stretches under sexual tension, and forms the sore there after a few days of incubation. The sore begins to grow and gets painful, and there are usually swellings of the lymphatic glands in the area – we call these swellings buboes – which break through the skin after a time and themselves turn into open sores. Before the invention of sulphonamide drugs chancroid was a most intractable form of venereal disease and kept spreading over the area of the genitals, where infection naturally started, until great damage was done. But now the sulphonamides cure almost every case very quickly. Chancroid can't be classed as a very frequently encountered or a very powerful medical enemy today – unless, of course, it's left untreated for too long, as it often is in relatively uncivilized communities.

'Now Gonorrhoea. The word itself is derived from a Greek word that meant "a flow of seed". The Greeks used it because they thought that the discharge that is characteristic of the disease was escaping semen. The infective organism is a coccus called *Neisseria gonorrhoeae*. It's very small, spherical in shape, and if you magnify it a thousand times under a microscope it looks like two kidney beans facing each other. It begins to take effect after an incubation period of a few days. Its hide-out is in dead white blood cells or pus and it causes an unpleasant discharge from the urethra – that is the passage leading from the bladder – and a smarting feeling due to inflammation; and if it's left untreated the infection can spread locally back into the bladder, prostate, kidneys, womb, ovaries, and so on. In both sexes the reproductive organs are often affected and it is a common cause of sterility. If a pregnant woman is infected her baby may be blinded through contact with the continual discharge in the passage the baby passes through to be born; and a man can suffer the considerable agonies of stricture – that is inability to pass water – if the coccus gets too firm a grip. Also, it can be carried by the circulating system all over the body and cause rheumatism, fibrositis, and eye and heart troubles. Gonorrhoea isn't really a dangerous disease if treated quickly and adequately, but it's only since the introduction of the sulphonamides and penicillin that we've been able to treat it properly. You'll find instructions about treatment in the book of Leviticus in the Bible – most of it being along the lines of constant disinfection and especial cleanliness – and it's true to say that such treatment, in essence, was all there was until this century. Sandalwood oil and permanganate of potash were often used, but all they really accomplished was a mild cleansing. The sulphonamides, when they came, were enormously effective but sometimes had unfortunate side effects; but penicillin has proved to be the most effective treatment of all, although evidence is gathering that the coccus is developing a resistance to it.

'Now then : Syphilis. This is really the biggest enemy. Conquerable indeed, but a difficult fellow. Its name (we may as well keep this account orderly) is relatively new. The Council of Trent had a sort of staff doctor whose name was Hieronymus Fracastorius, and in fifteen-thirty he published a poem called "Syphilis Sive Morbus Gallicus". I don't know whether it's certain that he wrote it, but he had it printed and referred back to it in a medical treatise he wrote in fifteen-forty-six. It was a poem telling, in part, the story of how Syphilus, a Greek shepherd boy, angered the god Apollo and was given the disease as a punishment. The infection he got in the myth may or may not have been the syphilis we know today, but evidently Fracastorius inferred some symptoms that were common in the plague of syphilis that hit Europe at the end of the fifteenth century and thought it would be a good name to give the disease. Up till then it had been called by hundreds of different names, a great many of them accusingly geographical, which resulted in the English calling it "the French disease", the French calling it "mal de Naples", the Poles calling it "the German illness", the Tahitians calling it "the English pox", and so on. Anyway, it's been called by Fracastorius's name ever since – except by people who call it, rather imprecisely, "the pox". It is *a* pox of course – all poxes are characterized by sores and eruptions – but there are a good many others – smallpox, chickenpox, and so on – and it's just taking the line of least resistance to call it "the pox". Anyway, whatever you call it it's caused by the organism I've mentioned before – *Spirochaeta pallida*. This is a germ of the genus *Treponema,* which comprises all the parasites that move in a wiggling way and live in warm-blooded creatures like man. *Pallida* is a corkscrew-shaped creature, dead white in colour, with tapering ends and a few whiskers sprouting all over its body. It moves spirally, boring through the tissues, but it also undulates like a snake, turning at quite sharp angles sometimes. Quite an active chap, you see. Unlike the cocci of gonorrhoea and chancroid it doesn't limit its activities. It can attack any organ, system, or tissue throughout the body except the hair, fingernails, and toenails; and for that reason it often causes trouble in diagnosis : it can, you see, imitate the symptoms of so many other illnesses. So if you've caught it and go to a doctor when all the characteristic symptoms of its first and second stages – the sores, rashes, and swellings – have died out, he may well be confused and diagnose a complaint that *pallida* is merely imitating the symptoms of. This is why it often got confused with leprosy, bubonic plague and other totally different diseases in the past. Nowadays there are tests to confirm the presence of

Syphilis, but the doctor may well have no cause to make any of
them if the patient denies ever having had any of the early symptoms – which he often does. One of the other remarkable
characteristics of *pallida* is that it may lie dormant – apparently
dead – in any part of the body for years and suddenly get stirred
into activity by some apparently irrelevant happening – it might
be a mild blow or something like that. Anyone infected with it
may have enough bodily resistance, even without treatment, to
apparently conquer its effects. But it can lie low and live in an
inactive state for a long time and then start its burrowing all
over again. Oh, I tell you, it's a marvellous organism.' The
Doctor leaned forward to emphasize the remarkable nature of
his enemy. Then he continued. 'As I said before, I think treatment is imperative. I've known too many cases of people who
have died of some organic disease brought on by syphilis.
Although the direct cause of death has been the failure of a
particular organ or system, it is the virulent attack of *pallida* that
has caused the failure. Napoleon is, in my view, a case in point;
but I daresay you'd like to keep particular cases out of a dis-
cussion about the general picture, as you call it.'

This seemed to me to be a good plan; but I hadn't in any
case touched on the other venereal disease I'd heard of – Lym-
phogranuloma inguinale. Not that I set much store by its importance nowadays; its complex name – not nearly so ugly as the
others – had really attracted my laymen's ill-informed attention
and I wanted to know if, as I understood, it was nowadays
confined to tropical climates.

'Not by any means,' the Doctor said. 'The tropics, Russia,
Germany, France – it's more frequent there than in Britain, but
it certainly happens here, though rarely. As you can guess from
the name, its effect is mainly on the lymphatic glands near the
genitals – the groin is the inguinal area – and it can have the
most devastating effects : for instance, a most painful stricture of
the rectum, or an elephantiasis of the genital organs. You know
what I mean?'

'Presumably some kind of freakish enlargement,' I said. I

went on to tell him that during a visit to East Africa I had seen an African of middle age so afflicted in this way that he had had to support the weight of his genitals in a little wheelbarrow which he had to push before him as he walked. Nor was I the only one to see this freakish enlargement. Sir Richard Burton, arriving in Zanzibar in 1856 to set out on his marvellous exploration in search of the source of the Nile, noted 'the prevalence of urinary and genital diseases ... Syphilis spreads wide ... The "black lion" as it is popularly called . . . will destroy the parts affected in three weeks: secondaries are to be feared; noses disappear, the hair falls off, and rheumatism and spreading ulcers result. Gonorrhoea is so common that it is hardly considered a disease ... Elephantiasis, especially of the scrotum, afflicts, it is calculated, twenty per cent of the inhabitants . . . The scrotum will often reach the knees; I heard of one case measuring in circumference forty-one inches, more than the patient's body, whilst its length (thirty-three inches) touched the ground. There is no cure and the cause is unknown. The people attribute it to the water.' When I paraphrased this and mentioned my own African observation the Doctor said :

'That's the thing. There's also another condition called Granuloma without the "Lympho" prefix. This one is characterized by ulcerated granulations spreading from the groin to the genitals and buttocks. Then there's Vincent's Infection, a severe inflammation or ulceration in the throat and mouth; but you can clear that up in a very short time. All these venereal diseases other than syphilis and gonorrhoea are relatively uncommon, though. Gonorrhoea is the second most prevalent disease in the world – measles is the most prevalent. If you want to present the true picture syphilis and gonorrhoea should be slap in the middle of it. They're the important ones. Even chancroid, which is important medically because of the ease with which it can be confused with syphilis, is comparatively rare in Britain today.'

He hesitated, took out his reading glasses and polished them on the silk handkerchief, then returned them to the breast pocket. 'There was something else ... oh yes, nothing important

... a small etymological problem rather than a medical one. The vulgar synonym for gonorrhoea is of course "clap", but no one seems to be quite sure why. Doctor Johnson wrote a poem called "London" in which there was a line that went "They sing, they dance, clean shoes, or cure a clap", but it had been used as standard English a long time before that – fifteen-eighty-seven, in fact (it only became a vulgar word in the Victorian age), and the general feeling is that it derives from the French "clapoir", which means a bubo or swelling, or "clapier" which means a brothel. Do you think that likely?'

It seemed to me most probable, and I said so.

'Good, good. You're a man of words. I'm glad to have it confirmed by you.'

It was confirmed not just by me but by that doyen of English philology, Mr Eric Partridge; also by the late Mr Noah Webster's dictionary – though not by the Oxford, which ignored the whole matter of clap's etymology. And on my next visit I offered the Doctor these confirmations. He seemed absurdly pleased with the trivial service I had performed for him and chuckled away gleefully. 'It's another little bit to add to the jigsaw,' he said.

The jigsaw so far assembled seemed to have most of its few pieces in the right places. I understood many things about the venereal diseases that I had not understood before, and I thought about two tittles more compassionately of Hitler than I had thought before. With the Doctor acting as an elucidating guide I had cleared a way through the jungle of such tomes as Stokes's *Modern Clinical Syphilology*; and I had begun to feel involved – though fortunately not apprehensive – whenever my glance encountered one of those admonitory notices about venereal diseases that one may see among the graffiti in any London public lavatory. But I felt that the picture of the greater enemy was still extremely shadowy. It had germs in it but no people. And although I could have taken countless casebook histories from Stokes, David Thomson's *Gonorrhoea*, Schamberg and Wright's *Treatment of Syphilis*, and Moore's *The Modern Treatment of Syphilis*, I found these histories for the most part anonymous and elaborately clinical. For example : 'A soldier on the third day of his urethral infection was admitted to hospital with an eruption on his chest, face, arms, and legs. This eruption was composed of rounded and polymorphous erythematous patches. He had fever (102.9° F.), and within forty-eight hours the erythema had become general, and assumed a bullous character. The various bullae were filled with a purulent liquid, which in some instances was bloodstained. His face, which was remarkably red, became oedematous, and conjunctivitis supervened. Gradually the various patches underwent desquamation, and the bullae were superseded by scabs. The fever remained at 102° F. for eleven days, and the patient was very depressed and feeble. The nature of the complaint remained obscure for a week, until cultures were made from the blood which revealed the presence of the gonococcus.' This sort of thing left me unsurprised that the soldier should be depressed and feeble but curious as to what lecherous revels had led him to his unhappy and oedematous condition. This curiosity, I knew, could never be satisfied by Thomson's chapter on 'General or Systemic gonorrhoeal infections' in which the soldier had made his fleeting appearance, for Thomson was concerned with effects and their causes, and surely was completely indifferent to the soldier's private life. I determined to ask the Doctor on my next visit if I could glimpse through his eyes any cases he knew of that had been touched with drama or poetry or that had had for him anything other than a clinical interest.

We were stirring the sugar in the cups of tea Veronica, his secretary, had brought in when I asked him this. 'Why yes,' he said, 'I daresay I can oblige you with a tale or two. I must refresh my memory with a look at my files; but first, I think, while we're drinking our tea I might tell you a story that fits in very well with the drinking of tea. You may even find it dramatic in its small way.'

He handed me the plate of biscuits and I took one and put it in the saucer while he groped about in his memory for the date of the incident he wanted to report. 'About nineteen-twenty-two or -three it would be,' he said. 'Veronica has been with me for thirty years, but before that she was a dispenser at the hospital where I had my clinic, and there she worked for me and my closest colleague of the time – call him Doctor Brown if you're still edging round real names. She always made us both cups of tea in her dispensary in the afternoon, then brought them to Brown and me in our adjoining consulting rooms between appointments. The appointments book was always crowded, but I had time to gulp down the tea while one patient was being shown out and another in from the waiting-room at the end of the corridor.

'Well, on this particular day she brought the cup in as usual and said that the next patient would be on his way in half a minute. Allowing for the length of the corridor I would have to drink it in about forty-five seconds flat. This I did. It was both hot and bitter, and I remember thinking that it was an unusual stinging bitterness, not at all like the taste associated with lack of sugar. But I just assumed that Veronica had forgotten to put in my usual generous amount, finished the tea and saw to my next patient. A little later I took the cup back to Veronica's dispensary and asked what she'd done to make it so spitefully bitter. She said she'd put the usual amount of sugar in it but that perhaps the pot had acquired a coating of tannin and needed scouring. Anyway, I returned to my room and was busily completing some patients' records when Doctor Brown came in, looked at me in a rather puzzled fashion, and asked me for a cigarette. I gave him one and he asked me if I were well and fit. I told him I was but didn't like the weather and he went away. Twenty minutes later he was back asking me for another cigarette and repeating his question about my health. I thought this was all leading up to some joke or other and didn't enquire too closely about the reasons for his concern.

'But when I left to go home after the last patient of the day Veronica called me into her dispensary. She looked shocked.

She pointed to two glass jars on her work bench. They were identical in shape and size and the contents looked the same – like granulated sugar. Then she told me what a dreadful thing had happened, what a frightful mistake she had made. She had put a heaped teaspoonful of the wrong powder into my tea. It was Sodium nitroprusside, which she had been using to test specimens. I won't blind you with science, but Sodium nitroprusside is virtually prussic acid, only rather more deadly, and with no known antidote. When I'd complained about the bitter tea she realized what she'd done, called Doctor Brown and been told that there was absolutely nothing whatever to be done, that the action of nitroprusside was instantaneous and that by that time I must be dead on the floor. He volunteered to go and find out for her. Finding me alive he could only suppose that Veronica had made a mistake and returned to the dispensary to reassure her. But there was no doubt : the dregs of my cup were full of nitroprusside. So he came along again to prod me as I lay dead on the floor and again had to ask me for a cigarette to excuse his visit.

' "Well," I said to Veronica, "I feel all right. I'll go along to the library before dinner and find out just exactly why your attempt to kill me didn't come off. There must be more to sodium nitroprusside than we know of. All the same,' I told her, "I hope you'll be more careful in future." '

At this stage of the Doctor's anecdote I put my teacup down with some dismay, hoping that Veronica had taken some notice of the Doctor's admonition. The Doctor leaned forward with his hands on his knees and continued :

'On my way to the library I began to feel a bit off-colour; nothing serious, no definite symptoms such as nausea or sickness, just a general sensation of being ill – an odd intangible feeling of trepidation which I knew was not psychological or temperamental but an overall tissue reaction throughout my body. But it didn't compel me to lie down or even stop walking. I called in at the library of the Royal Society of Medicine and looked up everything I could find on sodium nitroprusside and found that it was just as deadly as we'd supposed it to be, with no known antidote. But, the books said, there was about one person in twenty thousand who was naturally immune.

'Well, you know, I couldn't really believe I was the lucky one in twenty thousand. Life being such a very chancy and evanescent fribble we always tend to think that the calamities of life, and even death itself, always happen to the other chap, never to oneself. Yet here was I simply unable to believe that I had escaped calamity by such a long shot. I needed confirmation, indeed, that I was still alive.

'I decided to consult an old friend of mine, Sir Bernard Spilsbury, who was, as you know, a toxicologist so eminent that his word couldn't be contested on anything whatever to do with poisons. I knew he habitually left his laboratory in Hampstead to dine at the Junior Carlton Cub and afterward sat in a favourite armchair drinking a glass of port. I went along to the Carlton and there, sure enough, I found him. I told him my story and he declared that the books were right, that there *was* one person in twenty thousand who was naturally immune, and that for every one of the other nineteen thousand nine hundred and ninety-nine a single grain of sodium nitroprusside is lethal – instant death the moment it touches the tongue, and no known antidote. "Without doubt you're one of the lucky ones," he said, "because there's no other possible explanation. Now you must have a glass of port with me to celebrate your miraculous escape." Which I did.' He leaned back and laughed heartily. 'So it's no use anyone ever trying to poison me that way.'

In a few minutes Veronica came in to collect the tray. She was, for a woman, very tall – taller than the doctor – and had fresh pink cheeks and centre-parted grey hair twirled into a neat bun. The Doctor told her that he had been telling me the anecdote about her lapse and she held up her hands in horror. 'What a terrible day that was,' she said. 'I'm sure I could have been arrested for *manslaughter*. Oh, it was a terrible day.' She departed, still ruminating on the horror of the day.

'She doesn't do any dispensing now,' the Doctor said with

what I took to be a reassuring tone. He then continued: 'Now, you were asking me whether I could refer to any cases that had a dramatic or poetic interest. One that I suppose you'd call somewhat dramatic has just crossed my mind.'

He went on to tell me, in the impartial tone one might use to communicate a recipe for sago pudding, of an event belonging to the days when he was in charge of a V.D. Clinic. One of his patients was a man of seventeen stones or more, with strength to match; but his physical strength was apparently not matched by his common sense – he caught gonorrhoea from a prostitute in a sleazy part of London and turned up at the Doctor's clinic for treatment. 'He was full of the most diabolical threats as to what he would do to the girl if ever he came across her again and I told him not to be so foolish, since he'd soon be cured. Which he was.' After his cure, however, the man's vengeful thoughts must have lain dormant in his mind for some time. Then, quite by chance – since this time he was in a completely different and rather posher suburb – he met the girl again. He recognized her instantly, stopped her, and began to threaten her. This being done in a loud voice the girl became somewhat alarmed. There was a social gulf between her old beat and the new residential area, and she had bridged this with great effort, and didn't want to be shunned now because of the unreasoning vitriolics of an old customer. She managed to calm him temporarily by bursting into tears – she was aware that already curtains were twitching at windows – and then made him an offer. If he would come back with her now, she said, she would offer him solace in a *different* way, and, as a consolation, for free. '*You* know,' she added, pointing to her mouth. This offer of fellatio appealed to him and he forgivingly returned with the girl to her room. To give him the promised oral stimulation she knelt between his legs while he sat in a chair, and this posture proved to be disastrous, for, while experiencing the ecstasy of her orgasm, she involuntarily and uncontrollably bit into his pudendum and was quite unable to relax her grip. Raging with pain and anger the man seized her by the throat and flung her to the floor. He must by chance have applied his great strength to the vital structures in the neck and so occluded the two carotid arteries that carry the blood to the brain, thus killing her instantly. After a while the man's brain cleared. He was terrified – 'as who wouldn't be looking at a dead girl lying on the floor in front of you?' the Doctor said – but he managed to summon up enough sense to make a decision. He left everything exactly as it was, bound up his injured member with a handkerchief, and went straight round to the police station. There he told his story perfectly truthfully and had no difficulty in convincing the Station Sergeant. The police accompanied him back to the room, where it was confirmed that the dead girl was a known prostitute. Because of his wise confession and the special circumstances he was treated as lightly as the law allowed. 'Now would you call that dramatic?' the Doctor concluded.

I said yes, in its somewhat sordid, horror-comic manner, I supposed it was dramatic. I had indeed noticed before, when talking with other doctors of my acquaintance, that they had many sad, lurid little anecdotes to relate and that these invariably raised an embarrassed titter in non-medical company. For the doctors, however, they were stripped of their prurience. They were plain facts untinged by social disapproval. 'This is what happened,' they always seemed to be saying. 'The ravages of sickness or the instincts of lust take no account of codes of social behaviour – which are, anyway, extremely parochial and continually changing, so that what is supposed to disgust in Britain today may have been considered erotically beautiful in India for a thousand years.' I wasn't disgusted by the Doctor's tale; but nor was I carried along by any feeling of suspense. I said it seemed to me just sad that this anonymous woman should die with such lack of dignity in a squalid back room and be shovelled off into some equally anonymous patch of earth – or, more probably, used as a cadaver for students to dissect in a hospital mortuary.

'This simply means,' the Doctor said lightly, 'that in the escritoire of life this anecdote belongs in the pigeonhole marked "tragedy". For us doctors, though, there's rarely any profit to be gained by pigeonholing cases according to their emotional impact. Diagnosis, prognosis, cure – these are the important things for us. At the time one may think "the circumstances that brought this poor woman to this state are tragic", or "what is society about to permit conditions in which this man must suffer?" But these considerations are always peripheral. The thing is to *cure,* not to concern ourselves with putting cases into life's innumerable compartments. The writers and artists must do that. We have to remain detached, clinical. That's why we so often get accused of being hard and unsympathetic. We're not, of course; but sympathy is an emotion and medicine is a science and you can't mix the two in the wrong proportions. Anyway, I'll leave you to stick the labels on – "sad", "dramatic", "tragic", or what you will.'

That afternoon I heard no more from the Doctor. I had had it on my mind for some time that although, like everybody else, I'd heard of the Hippocratic oath which is sworn by most doctors when they begin practice, I'd never known what form it took, and I decided to go to a nearby library and look it up rather than weary the Doctor with routine questions that could as easily be answered in a routine way. I expected it to pin down the ethics of medical practice, and in its way it did.

'I swear,' the oath taker says, 'by Apollo the healer, and Asklapios, and Hygeia, and Panacea and all the gods and goddesses .  . that, according to my ability and judgement, I will keep this Oath and this stipulation – to reckon him who taught me this Art as dear to me as those who bore me ... to look upon his offspring as my own brothers, and to teach them this Art, if they would learn it, without fee or stipulation. By precept, lecture, and all other modes of instruction, I will impart a knowledge of the Art to my own sons, and those of my teacher, and to disciples bound by a stipulation and oath according to the law of medicine, but to none other. I will follow that system of regimen which, according to my ability and judgement, I consider for the benefit of my patients, and abstain from what-

ever is deleterious and mischievous. I will give no deadly medicine to anyone if asked, nor suggest any such counsel; nor will
I aid a woman to produce abortion. With purity and holiness
I will pass my life and practise my Art . . . into whatever houses
I enter, I will go there for the benefit of the sick, and will
abstain from every act of mischief and corruption; and above
all from seduction . . . Whatever in my professional practice –
or even not in connection with it – I see or hear in the lives of
men which ought not to be spoken of abroad, I will not divulge,
deeming that on such matters we should be silent. While I keep
this Oath unviolated, may it be granted to me to enjoy life and
the practice of the Art, always respected among men, but should
I break or violate this Oath, may the reverse be my lot.'

Austere stuff. I readily saw that with such an oath nestling
in their ethics doctors were bound to keep the categorizing of
emotions severely at arm's length. For my oathless self no such
restriction obtained and I was able to ponder deeply the psychological significance of the next story the Doctor told me. Mercifully, I shall keep my ponderings to myself and just tell the story.

The Doctor had a patient, a very beautiful girl who had tired
of rural life and come to the city for life and excitement of a
kind she knew she would never experience in the country. She
had saved a little money and supported herself on this while she
looked for work. But though she was attractive she had none
of the practical qualities sought by city employers, and very soon
she had run through her savings and was on her beam ends. At
this stage the inevitable happened and she took to prostitution.
Celia – as I'll call her – was as inexperienced at this as she was at
everything else, and paid for her inexperience by becoming a
patient at the Doctor's Clinic. Cured, she decided to return to
the country, but on the very evening before she was due to do
so she met a man who was immediately attracted to her and
offered to set her up as his mistress. 'You can have a nice flat I
can lay hands on,' he told her, 'and you won't have to oblige
me more than twice a week. And I will of course give you a
regular allowance.'

It was a temptation she couldn't resist. She wisely insisted on her prospective paramour having an examination, but when the Doctor gave him a clean bill of health she didn't tinker with the proposition any further. 'This is what I came to town for – to live the life of a town lady. I shall be happy that way.'

'I hope you will be,' the Doctor told her. No doubt he thought it an unwise and unsatisfactory way of living, but that consideration had no clinical interest.

'At all events,' the Doctor said, 'it seemed settled for the time being. But of course she soon got bored and lonely. The man who was supporting her visited her only once or twice a week and she soon set about looking for additional men friends. It wasn't difficult to find them. Nor was it difficult to get them all to pay the rent and give her allowances. She cunningly saw to it that each one of them thought he was her only lover – which was simple enough, because women can so easily convince men (who are all egotistical and vain) that no other male on earth is of the slightest account. And she solved the practical problem of their avoiding meeting each other by arranging their visits at different times.' The Doctor rose and went to the tinkling telephone and had a five-minute conversation with someone about something incomprehensibly medical. He made some notes and returned to Celia. 'All this is very commonplace, as you must know. Country girl – wicked city – downfall: trite as they come. I've hundreds of such stories in my head. But as it happened this one turned out differently.'

He went on to explain that Celia's flat was on the top floor and all the floors below were offices, occupied only during the day – a great advantage in her case, for evening visitors never ran the risk of being seen as they went upstairs.

One of her customers – to whom I will give the epicene name of Leslie – was a sexual pervert. He was a transvestite and a flagellant. Normal sexual congress meant nothing to him. His visit always began with a complete stripping-off of his street clothes and a slow and loving re-dressing in women's garments. Celia was required to help him dress from the skin up in corset, brassière, panties, slip, and frock. She had caressingly to pull on his stockings and high-heeled shoes and adjust his wig. Then she would help him make up his face. She could increase his pleasure enormously by giving him some new item of underwear, or a new dress, to wear each week.

When the dressing up was completed Celia herself had to change into full riding kit – breeches, hunting boots with spurs – and arm herself with a horsewhip. Then Leslie had to be trussed up with rope in such a way that he couldn't escape. In this state he would lie on the floor while Celia, taunting him with his helplessness and her spurs, would whip him. The more she could impress on him that he would starve to death if she left him there, that he was completely in her power, the greater the masochistic pleasure he experienced and the harder grew his struggles to free himself from the confining ropes. It seems a painful and exhausting way of achieving sexual satisfaction; but I speak, of course, from a viewpoint different from Leslie's.

Anyway, Celia fulfilled her duty week after week and when Leslie had achieved what passed with him for an orgasm he went on his way, presumably rejoicing. But one evening while they were in the middle of this erotically curious performance there was an interruption: a heavy knocking at the door of the flat.

Naturally Celia thought it was one of her other lovers who had mistaken the date. She was perturbed but thought she could deal with the situation. She left Leslie lying on the floor in what was for him a state of *coitus interruptus,* hastily put on a long dressing-gown that covered her hunting clothes, and went to the door.

A policeman stood there. 'Madam,' he said, 'you must escape at once. One of the offices below has caught fire and the whole building is in danger. Come with me. Don't bother about anything. I'll see you down and out. There's a lot of smoke but you'll survive that.'

'I'll come,' she said; 'but first I must —'

'No, it's urgent,' the policeman said, and she could see that it was, for already wisps of smoke were visible on the stairway behind him. Her anxiety, though, was for Leslie: she neither wanted him to be burned alive nor to be seen by the policeman. She slammed the door in the officer's face and hurried back into the room. 'The building's on fire,' she said and flung herself down beside Leslie and frantically tried to undo the knots. At this he was more thrilled than ever, thinking it was a new idea of hers to frighten him, and struggled violently to free himself. His efforts were so great in his ecstasy that she found it impossible to loosen the knots. He was shrieking with masochistic pleasure and the more she tried to convince him that the fire was real the more he struggled and shouted.

Celia was beside herself with terror. She almost lost her head. At any moment someone might burst into the room and discover Leslie in his peculiar state. Strangely, the keeping of his secret seemed more important than the fire; she knew she must do something, but what?

She ran to the window and flung it open. There was a crowd in the street. A fire engine had arrived and a fire escape was being raised against the side of the building. A cloud of smoke billowed up from below and blew into the room, and it was this that convinced Leslie of the real danger.

He stopped struggling, his ecstasy turned to horror. Quickly Celia ran into the kitchen and returned with a carving knife. She hacked away at the cords and dress and got him into his overcoat to hide the feminine underclothes – there was no time to do anything more. Together they ran out of the flat and down the stairs, passing the firemen on the way. In the street the confusion was so great that they had no difficulty in escaping unnoticed into the crowd. As it happened, the fire was quite a small one, remarkable for the volume of its smoke more than anything else, and was quickly put out. Later that night they were allowed to return to the flat. Leslie dressed himself properly and went off, still trembling with terror, and Celia went to bed while fireman patrolled the building to make sure there were no further outbreaks. But the experience had shocked her so much that she couldn't sleep. The following morning she telephoned the Doctor and asked if she could see him at once.

'She simply wanted to tell me,' the Doctor said; 'to unburden her soul to someone she could trust. She looked so pale and tired and frightened that I scarcely recognized her. Oh, I know that's a conventional thing to say, a cliché. But it really was so. She had changed overnight – her expression, I mean. She'd always looked so gay and confident. Now she had become haggard and grey. She told me the whole story of her association with Leslie and said that she couldn't stand city life any more. Whatever the consequences at home she was going to return to the country and her parents. And indeed she did.'

'And Leslie?' I asked.

'Ah yes, Leslie. Well, at the time, while he was standing out in the street with Celia, watching the fire belching its smoke out of the building, he too was so fearful that he whispered to Celia that this was the end so far as his perversion was concerned. He declared he was cured and thankful for it. But it wasn't so. That type of sexual perversion is too deeply engrained. I put him in touch with a psychiatrist friend of mine who did everything he could. But the deviation wouldn't yield.' He turned and rummaged among a pile of *Lancets* and I got the impression that he was not rummaging in order to find something to show me but, rather, to change the key of the conversation. My impression was right. 'I said before that my enemy is a marvellous organism,' he said presently. 'But the mind too is a marvellous organism. Even without the injurious burrowings of *Spirochaeta pallida* it displays some strange characteristics – you have only to consider Leslie's. Then take my own mind for instance.' He paused as if to allow me to take it and examine it, then continued : 'I am, after all, a scientist with a scientific training that should enable me to *explain*. And indeed I can explain a great many chemical and organic things that happen to the human body and brain. I can repair injuries and account for illnesses and cure them sometimes. And to a large extent I know what goes on in the mind and why. But some things remain inexplicable. You would not, I imagine, suppose me subject to the kind of experiences often called "psychic"?'

I agreed that it was difficult to associate a man whose work was the examination of physical facts and real creatures (however microscopic), with the insubstantiality of psychic phenomena.

'All the same, this is true. I'll tell you some of them. At least it will demonstrate further what you no doubt know – because goodness knows it's been said often enough before: that man is a many-sided and remarkable creature. And I daresay you'll want a reasonably complete picture of me as well as of the enemy.' He chuckled. 'The protagonist and the antagonist in the middle of the stage with all the lights on, eh?'

I told him I'd do my best to record what the light revealed.

'Fine. Then you can show the protagonist and antagonist in battle, eh?' It obviously pleased him to think whimsically of himself and his enemy – an enemy at once great and minuscule – at battle in a lighted arena; his inability to think of himself as in any realistic sense a hero clearly keyed in very happily with such an absurdity.

Thereupon he launched into the first of a number of narratives that were to illustrate what we both came to call his 'marvellous' side – though he insisted we impose that nomenclature only as a ready term of reference to be applied to the mind of man in general, not to his in particular.

The Doctor is one of those people who, if asked, would claim that he never dreams – meaning that he rarely recalls on waking any dream he may have had while sleeping. But in 1935 occurred a vivid exception to this claim – 'It was in fact so vivid that it quite startled me.'

In this dream the Doctor knew himself to be a travel-stained and war-weary knight returning home after a long absence and many violent battles. He was wearing a tunic of chain mail and greaves of plate armour, a sword hung at his side, and he carried a kite-shaped shield. His armour and accoutrements were scarred and muddy and he was conscious of having lost both his horse and his servant.

He walked across rough moorland toward a river beyond which was a round hill surmounted by a massive castle with six towers arranged as two pairs in each of two diagonally opposite corners and two single towers forming the remaining corners of a square. This he knew in the dream to be his home.

Reaching the river he waded through rushes across it, noticing that the ducks took no alarm at his presence. He continued his way then over a field toward a wall forming part of the outer defences of the castle. This wall was of course too high to look over or climb, but he knew perfectly well that if he followed it to the left and round its curve he would come to a postern door – 'After all, it was my home; I was naturally familiar with the geography of the place.' But when he came to the door, though familiar with its exact shape and size before reaching it, on arrival he stood for a moment as it were *outside* the dream so that he was aware of being struck by its curious formation. 'I must have been for a tiny space on a different time level of the dream, as it were; otherwise it would scarcely have struck me as an unusual door.'

The door itself was enormously heavy – 'Though I seemed to push it open without trouble' – and the stone arch in which it swung was set with iron spikes and pointed flints that narrowed the doorway to a considerable extent and would limit the traffic through it to one person at a time. 'I remember being impressed, from my second time-level, by the crude beauty of the arrangement of spikes and stones.'

After passing through the door he crossed a green sward that sloped up to the twin towers between which was the entrance to the castle; then he traversed a cobbled causeway leading to a drawbridge guarding the entrance and, turning sharply right, reached a small door at the bottom of the right-hand tower. He entered through this door into an empty ground-floor chamber, climbed a stone spiral staircase, and entered a second chamber, rectangular in shape. This room was furnished in medieval style and occupied by five women all dressed in black robes, wimples, and conical hats. (I should perhaps mention parenthetically here that there seems to be some slight disparity in the costumes of the Doctor's dream : the mail armour with greaves – *id est* shin-guards – of plate, and the kite-shaped shield were typical of the late Norman period; while the woman's conical hat – not typically worn with a wimple – was fashionable some three hundred years later in the fifteenth century. But no matter : dreams can claim special privileges.) The women were characterized by mourning mien; without exception they looked woebegone; they were devoid of jewellery, and only their natural dignity prevented their appearing in the extreme of privation. Two were seated near the wide hearth to the right of the door, two stood in the centre of the room, and the fifth – a younger woman – stood behind him beside a slit-window. All of them were demonstrably glad and relieved to see him – 'But none of them moved toward me or showed any sign of affection. They seemed to have titular respect for me rather than affection, as though my rank entitled me to their fealty. I didn't recognize them or know their names. The only bit of dialogue in the dream was spoken by one of the older women. She said, "Thank heaven you are back. You are just in time. It" – and I knew that she meant the castle – "is still all yours. You have saved it, and us, in time." '

Immediately these words were spoken – they have an unmedieval ring – the dream ended. When he woke in the morning every detail remained vividly in his memory. He was convinced that the entire incident must have happened to him in fact as well as in the dream. But when and where? He had a clue to the period in the costumes and furnishings, but nothing whatever to indicate the locale of the castle.

A fortnight later the Doctor dreamed the same dream again. All the details were precisely as before. But this time he woke up, hurriedly fetched pencil and paper and made sketches of the castle and the postern door. He was so convinced that the castle existed in reality that he began a long search for it. Having no clue even to which country it was in – it might have been almost anywhere in Europe – he systematically began to plough through every likely book he could lay hands on, to haunt bookshops, libraries, picture galleries. But nothing resembling the castle of his dream came his way. He continued his search for two years, then dreamed the dream for the third and – a month later – for the fourth time. Again the episode was repeated in exact detail and he began to double his efforts to locate the castle.

Shortly after having the fourth dream the Doctor was telephoned by a lady who gave her name as Mrs Myfanwy Jones and asked if she might see him. She thought they might be distantly related, and, since the few brief details she gave led the Doctor to think her right, he made a rendezvous with her at the hotel where she was staying. She was in London only for twenty-four hours, to complete some business with her solicitor, and she had a bare half-hour free that same evening.

'When I got there,' the Doctor said, 'I waited for a few minutes – I was ahead of time – in the crowded lounge of the hotel wondering what the owner of the voice might be like. I was about to go to the inquiry desk and ask for Mrs Jones when a neat, attractive, dark-haired lady came up to me and said, "I knew you at once. I've seen you in my dreams."

'Well, we sat down for a quick talk and soon sorted out our relationship. We were in fact second cousins – though I had never known of her existence or been in touch with her branch of the family. Then, because she'd mentioned having seen me in her dreams I told her about my dream of the castle. She replied that in her dream she was leaning over the balustrade of a gallery or balcony waving to me – I was in the hall below – and calling, "Good hunting, Sire." As soon as she'd said the words, the silken veil attached to her conical hat drifted across her eyes and when she brushed it back I had gone from the hall.

'For the rest of the brief time left to us we talked as if we had known each other all our lives. She gave me her address, but we didn't arrange to meet or write. The address meant nothing to

me except that it was somewhere in Wales. I put it in my address book and forgot all about it. Curiously – I must have been
a bit slow-witted – in spite of the fact that I was so anxious to
trace my castle I never gave even a thought to any connection
between Myfanwy's dream and mine. I continued to try to find
the castle for several years – I didn't dream the dream again –
looking into book after book of photographs and pictures of
castles anywhere in the world. I knew I'd recognize it at once if
I saw a picture of it, but my hunt seemed all to no purpose. I
had no further communication with my cousin; and then all
our lives were disorganized by Hitler and the war.'

The Doctor rose from his chair and roamed angularly round
the room for a moment, prodding with his foot at a pile of files
that seemed in danger of toppling. Then he perched on the
edge of the sofa, leaned forward with his hands on his knees, and
sidetracked himself by telling me some stories of the war. These
I shall keep for their proper place. It was late afternoon before
I managed to get him to complete the castle story.

Its completion was begun in Cambridge. In 1944 the Doctor
was there making a round of bookshops and buying this and
that which he thought might be interesting. On a bookstall in
the market place he was attracted to a pile of miscellanea among
which nestled a linen-backed map. But he saw only the edges of
it and, because his arms were already laden with books, did not
stop to examine it. A fortnight later, however, he was in the
bookshop to which the stall belonged and saw the map again.
This time he opened it out. It was folded in three large panels
and proved to be a clean, perfectly preserved, coloured map of
North Wales. And in the lower left-hand corner, superimposed
as it were gratuitously on Cardigan Bay, was an engraving of
the Doctor's dream castle.

'The first glance told me without a shadow of doubt. That
recurring dream had incised the castle on my mind as sharply
as the engraver had etched into his plate. It *was* the same.'

But the search was not yet ended. Although, presumably, the
castle was somewhere in North Wales it was not named in the

engraving. There was only a complimentary dedication from the cartographer: 'To Sir Watkin Williams Wynn, Bart., this map of North Wales is respectfully inscribed by his obliged and obedient servant John Evans. Published as the Act directs, March 27th, 1797. Engraved by Robert Baugh.' An additional mystery lay in the fact that Sir Watkin Williams Wynn was an ancestor of the Doctor's – 'But I knew from family pictures all the residences in which that branch of the family had lived and not one of them corresponded to my castle. It seemed that the castle had been chosen as a subject for the decorative engraving quite fortuitously; there was no link that would help me. I was tantalizingly halted in my search once more. And although I pored avidly over every book I possessed showing castles in North Wales, nothing came to light. I had never in my life been to Wales, north or south, and I was far too busy at the time to go touring to satisfy such a trivial personal mystery.'

It looked as though the Doctor was stymied once again. The serendipity of his discovery of the map had seemingly stopped short. Then he suddenly recalled that Myfanwy Jones lived somewhere in Wales. He looked up her address and noted that it was St Asaph in Flintshire – one of the three northernmost counties of the principality. He made a tracing of the engraving of the castle and sent it off to her at once with a letter asking if she knew where it was. Her reply was astonishing.

'I must write you tonight,' she said. 'Your letter has given me much food for thought – far more than you can know.

'Your castle is none other than Rhuddlan Castle, under whose shadow my family has lived, to my knowledge, for six generations. Mine is the sixth to be born at St Asaph. The castle is about two hundred yards away . . Rhuddlan Castle is not now [as complete as in] the drawing, but there is not a shadow of doubt that it is Rhuddlan. I've shown it to three people and the answer is the same. It's a wonder I did not recognize it from my own dream.'

(The Doctor added in parenthesis: 'There wasn't any chance at all that I had seen pictures or listened to conversation that might have suggested the castle to me and lodged it in my brain ready for dreaming. And as I said before, I had never been to Wales in my life.')

At once he replied to Myfanwy's letter saying that he must go to the castle and see whether he could trace his steps as in the dream. She replied fixing a date for his visit and he went down to see her. After a good night's sleep he asked to be taken to the river so that he could be on the spot where his dream began.

The river was there all right (it was the Clwd), 'And,' the Doctor said, 'I found myself standing in the very field where the dream began, looking across the rushes to the green sward which rose steeply to the twin towers. The wall and the postern gate, though, had disappeared, and the towers were crumbling. I felt shocked and sad at their state of decay, but I was never in doubt about it being my dream castle.'

He went on to say how he crossed the river (much wider now than in the days of the dream), approached the castle and found the drawbridge still intact and the small door at the foot of the tower waiting for him. As in the dream he entered it and climbed the stone stairway to the room above; and there he found himself in the same rectangular room with the great hearth to the right of the door.

He was still sitting on the edge of the sofa, leaning forward with his hands on his knees. He repeated with enormous child-like pleasure: 'There is no doubt, no doubt at all: it was the identical room in which my dream had ended.'

I murmured that it was astonishing indeed.

'But why did I dream this dream?' he continued. 'Why did it recur three times? Why was it so intensely real that I was convinced of the necessity to search for the location of the castle? Why was I led to the map and why was that map so to speak "kept" for me because I had an armful of books the first time I saw it and didn't bother to open it? Why did my cousin come by seeming chance into my life? Did the episode of the dream actually happen to me in some previous life? The dream episode seems to have taken place some eight hundred years ago; and although my family pedigree goes back several hundred years before that I can't think that so-called "hereditary memory" would form such a long chain for my dream to pass along. No: such things are inexplicable.'

I ventured to suggest that J. W. Dunne in his *An Experiment With Time* had put forward the theory that might explain.

'Well of course,' he said. '*Might:* that's the operative word. There are several possible explanations. But a scientist is only fidgeted by probabilities. He likes to *know,* to be able to confirm the explanation with his microscope or by other means, so that there is no shadow of doubt. And I may add that this dream, this business of the castle, is not so odd as some of my other experiences which I shall tell you, and which, for want of a better word, I referred to as "psychic". I agree, of course, that it is part of the scheme of things that some things should remain un-revealed to us and that the mystery of the non-material mind is one of these. I think it was Voltaire who said, "Four thousand volumes of metaphysics will not teach us what the soul is," and Heraclitus who said, "You will not find its boundaries by travelling in any direction." And John Scott Haldane, who was modern and a physiologist and therefore had a very scientific approach to life, said that "the world, with all that lies within it, is a spiritual world". So it is really true, I think, that that part of the mind that is apart from the consciousness is a marvellous thing. Some part of all of us is neither material body nor conscious mind. And in me this part seems to be highly developed – just as my curious immunity to sodium nitroprusside is highly developed and equally inexplicable. I make no virtue of it. It simply is so. But then,' he added in a firm tone, 'if the human mind, in its material and abstract manifestations, is a marvellous organism, so, at their somewhat lower plane in the world of living creatures, are those organisms I've spent my working life doing battle with.' He chuckled again. 'Though I must say the arena hasn't always been very well lit.'

# 6 *The Trail of the Enemy*

The historical corners of the arena in which the Doctor and his predecessors have fought the venereal diseases are indeed somewhat ill lit. No one can tell you accurately when *Spirochaeta pallida, Neisseria gonorrhoeoa,* or *Haemophilis ducrevi* first began their attacks on man. A possibly syphilitic human bone believed to be of about 2,500 B.C. has been found in the Gobi desert, and similar discoveries have been made in Egypt and South America; Egypt – which had the earliest known civilization – has disgorged papyrii on which are written the symptoms of an illness called *uchedu* which affected the genitalia in a manner very similar to syphilis; India has a popular legend that the god Siva, whose symbol was a phallus, was infected with gonorrhoea; there is a record of an Assyrian heroine, Ukhat (a name meaning whore), who died of what appears to have been tabes dorsalis (or locomotor ataxia), which is syphilis of the spinal column; and the Bible mentions many people who suffered from maladies involving the symptoms of one or other of the venereal diseases (including King David, Abraham's wife Sarah, and Job) while in the Mosaic laws of Deuteronomy the penalties for uncleanly living include 'an inflammation . . . with an extreme burning' – which sounds very much like gonorrhoea. But there's very little unchallengeable evidence. Certainly gonorrhoea was rife among all the ancient civilized races; the symptoms described are unmistakable. Syphilis, however, is not so easily identifiable. The references in some old historical records and medical books to genital sores, swellings of the groin, fetid discharges, and crumbling of the flesh may have indicated the lesser venereal disease chancroid or non-venereal diseases like leprosy and yaws. Inevitably there is confusion due to ignorance

on the part of the doctors of those days, whose accumulation of
knowledge must have been continually retarded by the secrecy
of sufferers who feared social degradation, and by the fearful
attitude of societies that drove infected victims from their midst
and either stoned them to death or insisted that they live in
starving isolation. (An otherwise graceful Indian poet of 2400
B.C. says in a brutal tirade against those who suffer from a virulent skin disease, possibly leprosy: 'Let him whose body is
covered with pustules like the bubbles of foul air that arise from
the marshland and burst as they reach the surface, hide and live
in isolation on a dunghill, with pariah dogs and other filthy
beasts. Let us drive him from our village with stones and cover
him, who is himself nothing but living excrement, with ordure.
May the immortal rivers reject his filthy corpse.') It is easy to
understand such an attitude if not to condone it. The majority
of civilized people are fearful and disgusted by illnesses with ugly
or fetid manifestations; only relatively few – including, of course,
doctors – are merciful and curious enough to pursue knowledge
that will lead to cause and cure. And when they have to fight
ignorance and fear in their pursuit of knowledge their progress
is bound to be slow.

It is possible that syphilis as we know it didn't exist at all in
the ancient world. (That Gobi desert bone may be misdated by
several thousand years – such mistakes have occurred before : the
American archaeologist H. V. Williams admitted that he once
found a modern beer bottle in some gravel he had believed dated
from the middle of the glacial period.) But taking such scraps
of evidence as exist – particularly a Sanskrit medical book of
about 100 B.C., which described syphilitic symptoms almost unmistakably and in gruesome detail, – and piecing them together,
the likelihood is that it did.

The next time I visited the Doctor I asked him if he had any
views on the age and origin of the venereal diseases in general
and syphilis in particular. He shrewdly saw that I was trying,
for the information of my readers, to pin him down to some
authoritative statement – a common trick of reporters who like

to get scoops backed up with expert evidence. But he smilingly evaded my effort.

'If you mean to ask me, as I strongly suspect you do, for the actual birth certificates of the venereal germs, I'm afraid I can't help you. And if I could, the answer wouldn't be of more than academic interest. I don't think civilization would shake with astonishment and admiration if the *News of the World* were to run a story proving that the first venereal organism was born on the first Monday of the neolithic age. But if you also mean to invite me to indulge in speculation as to, for instance, whether or not syphilis was prevalent in Europe before the generally accepted date – which is the end of the fifteenth century – then I'll oblige.'

He obliged by marshalling and condensing for me the principal arguments in favour of the absence of syphilis in Europe prior to the end of the fifteenth century. There were three of them, and he opposed each with his counter argument as he reeled them off.

'The first claim is that there isn't any mention of any disease that looks like syphilis in any medical or other book until the end of the fifteenth century, the implication being that because there wasn't any mention of it it couldn't have existed. That's a pretty silly argument anyway. But in any case there *is* plenty of literature earlier than the fifteenth century that relates to what is very likely to have been syphilis – and in Europe. Hippocrates in Greece – who, incidentally described gonorrhoea with medical accuracy for the first time in the fifth century B.C. – also mentions another venereal disease involving rotting of the genitals which could easily have been syphilis. A Roman doctor called Aulus Cornelius Celsus described treatment with mercury for a disease with syphilitic symptoms in the first century A.D. And you've mentioned yourself the ancient Egyptian illness "uchedu", which was symptomized by inguinal swellings, genital sores, and disintegration of the tissues. A bit later – in the fourteenth century to be precise – the histories show that John of Gaunt and one of the Popes – I think it was Ubertinus the Eighth –

both died of illnesses that began with putrefaction and shrinkage of the genitals, which sounds to me much more like syphilis than gonorrhoea or chancroid. And later still, but long before the end of the fifteenth century, there are English laws forbidding brothel keepers to hold on the pay list any prostitute suffering from the rotting effects of the "nefandum unfirmitatum" – that is "the wicked disease". At that time gonorrhoea was always known as "the burning disease", so it seems that something quite different and more serious was meant. Then there are a good many what you might call implied references to syphilis in other historical literature. The Roman emperor Caligula, for instance, had some illness that resulted in his becoming a raving megalomaniac, very much like Hitler. So had the other Roman, Heliogabalus. The evidence in both cases points to the early stages of General Paralysis of the Insane, which is caused by syphilis. And if you do a little research I think you'll find that there are plenty of other medical and literary references to what seems to be syphilis.

'The second argument is that there isn't any pictorial representation of syphilis in art prior to the witching date of fourteen-ninety-three, meaning that if people had had the disease before that some artist is bound to have depicted its ravages in a portrait. That of course doesn't necessarily follow. But in any case there's the famous bust of Socrates in the Louvre which shows a definitely syphilitic nose.' He went on to explain that a syphilitic nose exhibits signs of collapse because *Spirochaeta pallida* has attacked the nasal septum – the wall immediately behind the nasal bones forming the bridge – and eaten it away, leaving the bridge and flesh to fall inward and the nostrils to face forward instead of downward.

'Then the fourteen-ninety-three people point to the fact that all the early sixteenth-century writers keep referring to syphilis as a "new" disease. Well, they were writing about the great epidemic that broke out just after Columbus's men returned from America. But that doesn't prove that it didn't exist in non-epidemic proportions long before that. Nor does the fact that there was no name for it until Fracastorius thought of one. Namelessness doesn't mean non-existence. It simply means that the great outbreak of fourteen-ninety-three brought the disease into such prominence that a name became necessary.'

The Doctor having disposed briefly of what one might call the non-evidence that syphilis didn't exist in Europe prior to 1493, I asked him to enlighten me on the importance of this date in syphilitic history. He refreshed his memory from a number of heavy tomes, sitting on the sofa and making notes the while, and in due course produced a résumé. This I filled out with some later investigations of my own and arrived at the following:

Christopher Columbus landed in what is now Haiti (he called it Española) in December, 1492, and arrived back in Spain in March, 1493. Almost at once he set sail again for Seville and Barcelona, which was full of mercenary troops who had settled there after the conquest of Granada in 1492. A Spanish doctor of the time, Ruy Diaz de Isla, writes of having treated innumerable sailors of Columbus's crews 'and the women they had used' for 'an hitherto unknown malady, which vastly spread to the soldiers of the garrison, knowing no bounds in speed and virulence. My opinion is,' De Isla goes on to say, 'that Admiral Columbus's sailors translated this malady from Española, and I have therefore named it for that island.' In the same year Charles VIII of France raised an army to invade Naples – an enterprise that took six months – and offered plenty of opportunities for the now disbanded Spanish mercenaries to join the French troops complete with their infection, which they presumably spread by way of the harlots who were always to be found among the camp-followers of such peripatetic armies. Once the French invaders reached Naples the Española disease again attracted medical attention – mainly because Caesar Borgia caught it and his doctor, Gaspare Torella by name, felt called upon to write a treatise on the diagnosis and treatment of what he called 'Pudendagrum seu Morbum Gallicum'. (His suggested treatment included sucking of the first sores 'by some person of worthless condition', poulticing with a live bisected frog, and immersion of the patient in the disembowelled body of a live mule.)

Two years later the disease – whatever it was – was carried into France by the same French mercenaries who had acquired it en route to Naples and were now returning, their king having taken alarm at the combined threats of the states of Milan and Venice and run them into defeat at the battle of Fornovo. The mercenaries were a motley lot, many of them being French only when French allegiance was profitable, and they went their cosmopolitan ways, taking their infection with them to the Lowlands, Germany, and Britain.

During the last years of the century the disease gained a ferocious grip on the whole of Europe. By then there was no doubt that it was a venereal disease, but the doctors identified it – wrongly – as a severe form of gonorrhoea, and serious physicians and quacks alike spent much time compounding remedies. (The genuine doctors were not always nearer successful treatment than the quacks. Gaspare Torella's treatment was far less likely to be effective than the recipe of a huckster of the time who had made an ointment by macerating together crushed bay-leaves, oil of scorpions, mercury, pork fat, and wood ash.) And the belief that the new disease had been imported from Española by Columbus's men was building up. It has now become firmly engrained in medical history, but is as controversial as the authorship of Shakespeare's plays.

The Doctor isn't alone in doubting the Columbian theory: Dr Gaston Vorberg, a German pathologist, has produced a long and learned book, *Uber den Ursprung der Syphilis* which offers a lot of evidence intended to deflate it. One of his contentions is that there is no direct proof that any Columbian sailor contracted syphilis from a Haitian woman. This is true but negative. However, Columbus's own log of the return voyage from Haiti, which lasted ten weeks, says that no one was sick except one old man with gravel [of the kidney]. There were forty-four sailors and ten captive Indians in the two ships *Santa Maria* and

*Niña,* and it seems improbable that manifestations of syphilis could have been either innocently or deliberately concealed in such little ships as these caravels – particularly as the Indians were naked. No one complained to anyone of any disease when the ships arrived at their home port of Palos on the fifteenth of March, 1493, and this is significant, for 'All the people,' says Columbus's son, 'received him and his men in procession, giving thanks to our Lord for this notable gift and victory, which promised so great an increase for the Christian religion and the estate of the Catholic Sovereigns. And all the citizens took pride in the fact that the Admiral had sailed from that place and that the greater and better part of the people who went with him came from there . . .' Sailors did a good deal of beefing about shipboard conditions in those days, and if most of them belonged to Palos they would doubtless have complained to the authorities if they'd had any illness to complain about. Also, the naked Indian captives were presented at Court, and there is no mention in any of the full descriptions of this ceremonial presentation that any of them were disfigured by sores or other characteristics of syphilis. Dr Vorberg thinks that the Columbian sailors may subsequently have been responsible for spreading typhoid and/or dysentery which they caught *after* their landing on the fifteenth of March, but he is firmly convinced that the occurrence of syphilis exclusively in their wake is mythical. He admits that they may have had a hand – along with Charles VIII's mercenaries – in the spreading of syphilis, but insists that they caught it initially during their junketings ashore in celebration of their return. By way of a payoff to his adduced evidence, Dr Vorberg then produces pictures of two undoubtedly syphilitic bones – a humerus and an ulna – which were excavated in 1872 from a burial cave in the Petit Morin valley and belong to the neolithic period.

My additional researches into the written evidence of the existence of syphilis in Europe prior to 1493 led me through many big volumes. The first of these was E. G. Brown's *Arabian Medicine,* where I learnt that after the Crusades of 1096–1270 there was a marked increase in 'leprosy' and 'lepers' were confined in lazarets – that is, hospitals for contagious diseases, the name deriving of course from the Lazarus of the Bible. They were buried in special cemeteries, where centuries later skulls with unquestionable syphilitic erosions were found. Among the specialists who found and examined them were two renowned pathologists, Professors Parsons and Shattuck. Professor Parsons says categorically: 'I *know* that [syphilis] was present, though rare, among the thousands of thirteenth-, fourteenth-, and fifteenth-century bones in the Church of St Leonard at Hythe in Kent.' He also draws attention to Chaucer's comment on the cook in the *Canterbury Tales*: 'But great harm was it as it thoughte me, that on his shin a mormal [ulcer] hadde he.' When I mentioned these dippings into medical books to the Doctor he recalled Professor Parsons easily. 'In my student days,' he said, 'I often watched Parsons examining these bones – cleaning, measuring, and studying them for hour after hour. I remember marvelling at his patience. No one would willingly have interrupted him while he was examining his bones. They were his speciality and hobby and he was as capable as anyone in the world of recognizing osseous syphilis. However, there's a slight chronological difficulty: Parsons says the bones were of the thirteenth, fourteenth, and fifteenth centuries. But we musn't forget that the Columbian epidemic began in England in fourteen-ninety-four, so by the year fifteen hundred there'd have been plenty of syphilitic bones in burial grounds. I don't know how sure Parsons was that the bones he examined were pre-Columbian, but I believe it's only since his day that we've been able to establish accurately the age of bones with scientific methods. I wish I'd asked him if he was sure of the dates of those bones but at that time I was scarcely even aware of the existence of syphilis, and certainly didn't know that its study was to become my life's work.'

Whatever the date of Professor Parsons' bones may have been, E. G. Brown goes on to add another jot of evidence. He says that the Crusaders brought back from the Holy Land a concoction called 'Saracen ointment' which contained mercury and was most effective in the treatment of what the doctors of the day thought was leprosy. One of these was a thirteenth-century medico named Theodorus, another was Bernard de Gordon. Dr Theodorus said in a treatise of 1303 that leprous women were venereally contagious. And Dr De Gordon said that leprosy was indigenous among prostitutes, and that their children might inherit it from them. But both doctors were writing under a misapprehension. Mercury is useless in the treatment of leprosy, which is in any case not inherited, nor is it venereal. Mercury is, however, very effective in the treatment of syphilis, which *can* be inherited. So it's most likely that their 'leprosy' was in fact syphilis.

In Stow's eighteenth-century *Survey of the Cities of London and Westminster* there are several references from which I infer that syphilis was about before the fifteenth century, even though often referred to as 'leprosy'. In 1321, for instance, Stow says that an English cardinal bought a brothel as an investment for the Church and because 'continence was in that day considered harmful and caused corruption of the flesh, so that the whore was regarded as a necessity. But the corruption of continence,' the cardinal warned his customer, 'was never so great as the corruption of the great pox, which is transmitted within the orifice and even by touch alone in bad cases.' Also in that age (the fourteenth century) Stow says that the celibate clergy kept housekeepers 'not as a source of pleasure but that super-abundant substance might not fall into corruption whereby evil disease would doubtless be increased among the honourable clergy.' These references were clearly to some venereal disease (whether or not it was thought to be leprosy), and since gonorrhoea had been world-widely known since the most ancient times it seems improbable that it would have rated all these special mentions. In any case, of course, its symptoms are completely different.

One way and another, and without promoting the seeming interminability of this inventory, it seems to me that *Spirochaeta pallida* had been living in Europe, as in most of the rest of the world, for a good deal longer than 450 years and, if Dr Vorberg's neolithic bone from the Petit Morin was mistakenly backdated, was probably brought into Europe from the far east during the time of the Crusades, when it became confused with leprosy; but I think there's not much doubt that its activities were sparsely distributed until the epidemic of 1493. Its comparative rarity was probably due to the fact that the great plagues of earlier years – leprosy, bubonic plague, and smallpox – accomplished much of what nature intended as a balancer of population and that syphilis conveniently anticipated and replaced these plagues as they gradually died out in Europe. It seems evident that it would not have gained a grip of epidemic proportions in 1493 if people had developed a natural resistance to it through previous inculcation on any widespread scale.

There may be a scarcity of pictorial and literary references to European syphilis prior to 1493, but there certainly isn't after. The Europe of the sixteenth century was scourged by the disease, and the licentiousness of the age was the best aid to its perpetuation. Artists began to portray its manifestations with increasing frequency and writers wrote about it as commonly as they write about homosexual love today. The German artist Albrecht Dürer wrote to his friend and patron Willibald Pirckheimer, 'My reverence to our prior. Tell him to pray for me to God that He may guard me, and especially from the French pox. Because I know nothing that I fear more, since almost everyone has it. Many people are quite eaten up with it and die.' God or the prior must have failed him, for he caught syphilis during his visit to Italy in 1495 and delineated its ravages in one of his drawings. (The malady, however, seems not to have affected his famous conversational bawdiness, for he's recorded as saying *inter alia* to Willibald, 'You stink so of whores that I can smell it over here' – a quote I bring in merely to be able to record William Conway's euphemistic 1889 translation: 'It strikes me that there is an odour of gallantry about you') The Italian sculptor Giovan Paracca sketched himself in the extremities of poverty, with a pox-ridden face, in the workhouse he died in. Matthias Grünewald's 'Temptation of Saint Anthony' shows a syphilitic demon. And Giuseppe Arcimboldo, one of the first surrealist painters, was commanded by the Emperor Maximilian to caricature a well-known doctor of the day whose face was ravaged by syphilis. He composed the face entirely of animal heads and bodies and in doing so achieved a remarkable effect in which the cutaneous activities of *Spirochaeta pallida* are horridly evident.

The writers who set forth the lives of painters and sculptors weren't stinted of syphilitic facts in their subjects' personal affairs. Many of the artists who didn't portray syphilis in their pictures clearly would have had every opportunity of doing so in self-portraits. Giovanni Baglione's biography of Taddeo Landini mentions that the 'good time he enjoyed brought him such an acute and terrible pox that his nose dropped off'. Giambattista Passeri says that Pieter van Laer, a fashionable painter from Harlem, 'caught a certain disease that brought him little delight although he had acquired it through his pleasures' and later died of it. Filippo Baldinucci says of the fresco painter Francesco Romanelli that 'away from his wife, he enjoyed the continuous company and intimate conversation of women, the fault lying with his fiery temperament which was much inclined toward amorous adventures . . . because of this he was assailed by the tormenting illness that usually accompanies such pastimes'. And Georgio Vasari, another addicted biographer of artists, says of the portrait painter Dominico Puligo that '[having associated] with gay and lighthearted companions, with musicians and fair ladies, he died in the year 1527, in the pursuit of a love affair, having caught the plague in the house of one of his mistresses'; while of Mariotto Albertinelli, a painter who specialized in holy pictures, he says that 'while in Viterbo he had several sweethearts to whom . . . he wanted to prove how good he was at the old game – but since he was neither young nor valiant enough for such enterprise he merely caught the pox and died of his complaint at the age of forty-five'.

It was by no means only heterosexual lust that contributed to the spread of syphilis. The fifteenth and sixteenth centuries were of course great times for homosexual relationships. And then, as now, the venereal diseases were as perniciously transmitted by sodomy as by heterosexual intercourse. The Florentine reformer and monk Girolamo Savonarola preached a sermon to the priests of his city on 1st November 1494 in which he said, 'Abandon, I tell you, your concubines and your beardless youths. Abandon, I say, that unspeakable vice, abandon that abominable vice that has brought God's wrath upon you, or else: woe, woe to you!' But woe in the form of syphilis was already upon them, and if he thought the scourge of the disease was going to be a purifying one he was mistaken. When he was burnt at the stake for heresy in 1498 a member of the Council of Ten, which had been formed 'to preserve the liberty and peace of the subjects of the republic and to protect them from the abuses of personal power', remarked to a fellow councillor, 'And now we can practise sodomy again.' In theory there were terrible punishments to be inflicted on male prostitutes or their pimps, including castration, the rack and thumbscrew, the severing of hands and feet, and the burning alive of the culprits in any house in which they were discovered *flagrante delicto*. But the theory was not implemented by practice. Female prostitutes wore male clothing to attract customers and revealed their sex only when they'd struck their bargains, compensating the deceived men with intercourse *per anum* or with the dildoe or artificial phallus. And the general licentiousness of the age was encouraged by the personal lecheries of popes, princes, noblemen, and the judiciary, as well as by the populace. In every way *Spirochaeta pallida* had opportunities for its corruptive burrowings. And many years passed before the human body built up enough inherent resistance for the enemy's effects to become slowed down – though, as the Doctor says, unaided by treatment the body never wins; it merely occasionally harbours the organism long enough, without *apparently* disastrous effects, for its defeat to be believed in.

Punishment rather than prophylaxis – or, only slightly more

lenient, punishment combined with prophylaxis – appears to have been socially encouraged whenever the opponents of licentiousness could get a word in edgewise. Syphilitics were vilified as lepers were, had no legal redress against banishment or an administration's refusal to let them work for a living, and in some places were stoned to death or otherwise ceremoniously murdered – as for instance in Transylvania and its sovereign state Turkey. Scotland – via which the epidemic was introduced into Britain by mercenaries returning from Charles VIII's disbanded army – took stern but not murderous measures specifically against syphilis as early as 1497. In that year both Edinburgh and Aberdeen decreed that prostitutes suffering from the 'new' disease should be banished to the island of Inchkeith in the Firth of Forth. (This was the island to which James IV, that king of wide interests, sent two infant children in the charge of a dumb foster mother, his object being to discover whether they could learn to talk without tuition. They were supposed later to have learnt to speak 'very good Hebrew'; maybe the banished prostitutes had something to do with their achievement.) By their deportation order the elders and lawyers were simply interpreting literally God's words to Moses, recorded in the fifth chapter of Numbers: 'Command the children of Israel, that they put out of the camp every leper . . . and every one that is defiled . . . both male and female shall ye put out, without the camp shall ye put them; that they defile not their camps, in the midst whereof I dwell.'

London and Paris too had their ordinances and places of banishment for the defiled at a very early date; and although it's obvious that ignorance caused much confusion between syphilis and leprosy – and probably yaws – there are insistent references in the statutes to the brothels of medieval days being breeding grounds for contagious diseases. Since leprosy in its infectious form is visibly repellent, while syphilis may often be undetectable without close examination, leprous prostitutes are unlikely to have found much custom, so the lawmakers were clearly including venereal diseases in their segregational ordinances, even if they didn't know it.

There were lazar houses for the infected in Southwark, Stratford-at-Bow, and Lambeth – all districts that were notorious for their iniquitous brothels and criminals' hideouts. Bishops and nuns financed and staffed the lazarets (and financed the brothels), and even after Wat Tyler's peasants' revolt in 1381 in which much of Lambeth and Southwark was burnt and pillaged, they were quickly rebuilt – 'the stews [brothels] first, so that the lazar houses might not go customless for a Winchester Goose'. ('Winchester Goose' was the term applied to a whore in one of the Bishop of Winchester's brothels. Shakespeare uses it in *Troilus and Cressida*.) The lazaret in Southwark was called 'Le Loke', meaning enclosure (the modern term Lock Hospital is derived from it) and was founded in consequence of a command of Edward III in 1346, who had the Mayor and Sheriffs of London proclaim in every ward of the city, 'All defiled persons inhabiting here should avoid within fifteen days next; and that no man suffer any defiled person to abide within his house, and to incur the King's farther displeasure; all to be removed to some Out-Places of the Fields, from the Haunt or Company of Sound People, until lazar houses are builded for them.'

The Provost of Paris, in an ordinance of April 1488, enjoined all defiled persons to leave the city in consequence of 'the sickness of the king [Charles VIII], who has the smallpox or a new malady now beginning in Europe'. Leprosy was already rife in Paris at that time, so presumably some different form of contamination was feared. If this was syphilis it's another nail in the coffin of the Columbian theory, for Columbus had four years to go before he began his voyage of discovery.

It's difficult to pin down the name of the doctor who established that syphilis was different from leprosy, yaws, smallpox, or any of the other non-venereal maladies exhibiting putrescent flesh. Probably Fracastorius had as much to do with the discovery as anyone. But having decided that it was different, the doctors went too far in their acceptance of it as a venereal disease and classified it as a severe form of gonorrhoea. This misapprehension persisted for three hundred years. It wasn't until 1860 that Philippe Ricord, a French surgeon of the Hôpital du Midi, proved that the organisms causing the two diseases are quite different (though in 1793 an English doctor, Benjamin Bell, had demonstrated that they probably were); and only in 1879 was the organism causing gonorrhoea finally isolated and named *Neisseria gonorrhoeae* by Albert Neisser of the Koch Institute for Infectious Diseases in Berlin. *Spirochaeta pallida* was identified even later – in 1905, by a German zoologist, Fritz Schaudinn. (The systematists who classify germ organisms confuse the lay mind by offering an alternative name for *Spirochaeta pallida*: this is *Treponema pallidum*, and designates a sub-class of one of five classes of spiral organisms. But *Spirochaeta* is much more commonly used and I'm sticking to it.)

During those three hundred years of general misapprehension there were, it is true, a number of doctors who suspected that syphilis was different from, and not a severe form of, gonorrhoea. But they were for the most part working on hunches and were continually bedevilled by the fact that infection by both diseases simultaneously was – and is – quite common. With two sets of symptoms manifested in one patient their uncertainty was understandable. Also, reactionary opinions were held by many leading medical men. One of these was John Hunter, a great man in medical history, who is generally regarded as the founder of modern scientific surgery but who nevertheless proved to be wrong about the common identity of syphilis and gonorrhoea. His mistake hastened his death, for in an attempt to prove his point he inoculated himself with the germs of gonorrhoea, not knowing that the patient from whom he took them was also a syphilitic. *Spirochaeta pallida* ate into his spinal cord and he contracted *Tabes dorsalis*. He died of heart failure accelerated by syphilis in 1793, so it was nearly a hundred years before the influence of his *Treatise on the Venereal Disease* was overcome by Ricord's demonstration.

Much of the haziness surrounding venereal and many other diseases was of course caused by the invisibility to the naked eye of causative germs. No satisfactory microscope existed until the end of the seventeenth century, so earlier doctors couldn't be blamed for failing to differentiate between invisible organisms. Their methods of analyzing and identifying germ-borne diseases were largely hit and miss, and treatment was equally empirical. Until the achievements of the great nineteenth-century researchers – Pasteur, Lister, Curé, and people of like eminence – had been completed, doctors had to rely on intuition and the published works of their predecessors. Fortunately for mankind, doctors are intuitive and tenacious people. Without knowing the appearance or habit of their enemy they have held fast to the trail of *Spirochaeta pallida* down long corridors of time and through countless mazes and dangers.

# 7 *Canicular Days*

One of the dangers of practising medicine is of course the probability of self-infection. Surgeons nowadays have a slight edge on their physician colleagues because their work, being concerned mainly with organic repairs and removals and injuries caused by violence of one kind or another, brings them into touch with fewer directly infectious illnesses. But until the Doctor's day, when specialization in venereal diseases began – he was one of the beginners – the treatment of V.D. called for surgery as much as for medicine. One of the oldest surgical operations is for the opening of swellings to allow the escape of poisons (poisons meant demons in primitive societies) and, swellings being characteristic of at least two of the venereal diseases, doctors who were especially skilled in the use of the knife were called upon as often as those who advocated medical rather than surgical treatment, and were equally endangered by the risk of infection. But nowadays, as I say, the venereal diseases have been transferred to the attention of physicians instead of surgeons, and I was anxious to know how the Doctor had fared in avoiding infection himself, since it was evident that he must have been in the path of the enemy many a time. No intrepid character myself, I had disturbing visions of armies of *Spirochaeta pallida,* borne perhaps by a minuscule drop of infected blood or pus, falling unnoticed on to clothing or furniture and later being picked up and entering the skin like gladiators in full marching order through one of those minute cracks or abrasions that flesh seems to be abundantly heir to. I recalled having chickenpox at the age of forty-five and being warned by my doctor not to post any letters or return any books to the library or otherwise chuck my infection at an unsuspecting public; and

when I saw my disgusting pustule-studded face in the shaving
mirror every morning I certainly didn't want to start an epidemic of such horrid aspect. And that was just a minor infection,
not likely to kill anyone. You may imagine that constant conversation with the Doctor, reinforced by a gallery of
photographs of syphilitic flesh – all of unchallengeable nastiness
– had unnerved me somewhat. Carefully disguising my concern
for myself in tender enquiry about him, I asked if and how he'd
managed to escape infection.

'So far,' he said. 'But I've had some nasty moments of
suspicion. Once, I remember, I felt a slight irritation under a
fingernail and discovered a tiny sore place. Having been continually busy for months examining hundreds of venereal
patients – palpating their flesh, injecting them, getting scrapings
of their sores and so on – I was a bit alarmed. I was in bed at
home at the time and it was in the middle of the night. But I had
to get up and dress and drive three miles to my hospital so that
I could confirm or allay my suspicions with a microscopic look
at the germs in that sore. But it was all right: a bit of bristle
from a nail brush had got into the skin and infected it slightly.
I didn't have to treat myself for sigma phi.' (The Doctor often
used the two Greek characters as a convenient code word for the
word syphilis.) 'A great many doctors aren't so lucky, though.
I've got some figures somewhere that will interest you.' He loped
about the room opening drawers and peering into folders stuffed
with cuttings from *The British Journal of Venereal Diseases,* a
publication I had frequent recourse to in my subsequent researches. Eventually he found a slip of paper with some written
notes. 'There you are: I worked it out that in one year – nine-
teen-fifty-six – about one sixteenth of all my venereal patients
were doctors and dentists who'd been infected in the course of
duty. Fortunately, medical chaps have the sense to have themselves treated before things go too far, which is more than can be
said for a lot of people. But it's a reminder of the occupational
hazards. Writers, now, don't have anything like that to contend
with.'

Since I'd spent half an hour that morning peering through a microscope at *Neisseria gonorrhœae* magnified seventeen hundred times (and still no bigger than a black pin's head in a red-stained agglomeration of pus cells), handling slides, and in general being terribly daring in the cause of literature, I wasn't so sure. 'Well I don't know,' I said. 'What about when I was finding out what *Spirochaeta* and *Neisseria* looked like this morning? Why, I might even now be teeming with V.D.'

'I don't think so,' he said dryly. 'Those were dead germs you were looking at. I'll show you some live ones next time you come and you can have some worthwhile qualms.'

But next time I went we talked about something different. I had encouraged him to tell me something about his youth, but he had been somewhat reluctant to stretch his recollections back too far. 'If you talk about your childhood,' he said, 'you run the risk of excruciating everybody with boredom unless you were in some way remarkable, which I wasn't. Nor was my life. As I told you, my father was a country solicitor who had what is euphemistically called "private means". My mother had too. But this didn't mean that we lived luxuriously. My brothers and sisters and I lived perfectly ordinary happy lives such as were lived by thousands of Victorian families. I suppose it was assumed that we boys would take up one of the "professions" – you know: the church, law, the army – but we were never bothered about it. My father believed in educating his children himself, and this he did very soundly. We were quizzed on every task he set us and couldn't get away with sloppy work. I believe I was fairly quick to learn because I had a retentive memory, and I loved Latin. (Maybe you'd better call this bit about my youth canicular days instead of dog days.) But there really isn't anything interesting to be said about me as a child. Things get a bit livelier when I'm in my 'teens, and once or twice there was even a touch of adventure.' He smiled recollectively, then switched back to solemn mien. 'Nothing, of course, so fraught with danger as your encounter with the dead germs the other day.'

He went on to tell me how, in 1910, when he was a student in

Germany, he was using the long vacation to extend his European travels and indulge his hobby of photography. 'I loved all kinds of sport: football, running, jumping, and boxing were all dear loves of mine; but photography was my favourite hobby. I'd learnt its attractions from my father, who was a brilliant amateur and had given me a tip-top camera as soon as I knew enough about the game to be able to use it properly. It was a press photographer's instrument, a Goertz-Anschütz focal-plane quarter-plate, and of course it would be considered terribly big and clumsy in these days of miniature cameras. But the results were marvellous, and I'd had an attachment fitted to enable me to change plates in daylight.

'I'd been to northern Italy and was making my way back home via Austria, Germany, and France. I boarded the train for Innsbruck at Bolzano with my camera and a light suitcase – my heavy stuff had gone on ahead of me – and found that there were very few passengers. In my compartment there was only one other – a rather jolly looking priest with a wrinkled sun-burnt face and a flowing cassock. We exchanged the usual greet-ings and settled in our corners without extending the conversa-tion. I wanted to look at the countryside and, if an opportunity arose, perhaps take a picture or two; and the priest was busy reading alternately from a missal and a newspaper.

'I saw nothing worth my photographic attention, so didn't bother to take my camera off the rack. Then, when we'd been travelling quite a while I began to notice signs beside the rail-way. They were painted in big letters and warned passengers that photography was forbidden on pain of fine or imprison-ment. I suppose the order was part of the general unrest of the time, the general feeling that war was approaching. I of course had no knowledge of any impending disaster – I was young and happy and never thought about international politics – but I hadn't any wish to contravene any regulations, so just went on enjoying the scenery and dozing a bit. Then I remembered I'd bought some new very fast plates in Italy and decided to slip one into my camera ready for use when we passed out of the secret zone or whatever it was that made the authorities so chary of photographers. I took the camera down off the rack, popped a new plate in, and put it back. That was all. But I suppose I must have aroused the priest's suspicions, for presently he left the compartment and didn't return. A bit later, though, two gendarmes appeared in the corridor, eyed me, and took up posts on each side of the door. I could see by their attitude that they weren't likely to let me leave the train without a grilling. I was suddenly alarmed. I could see myself being arrested as a spy and having my precious camera confiscated – particularly as the train passed through Franzenfeste, which, I remembered having heard, was a newly fortified town of military importance at the frontier, a key fortress guarding the Dolomites. Evidently the priest had told them that I was loading my camera in preparation for Franzenfeste.

'I started wondering how unpleasant all this might be and how it would delay my itinerary. As you know, an Englishman can't bear to have his plans upset by nonsensical foreign regulations. In the circumstances it seemed to me best simply to disappear by jumping off the train. This wasn't so easy, however. The train was going too fast, for one thing; and for another, the gendarmes were still posted at the corridor door and could hardly fail to see me if I hopped it out of the opposite door. But fortunately the train began to slow down at that moment. It was taking one of those long mountain curves, and – also very fortunately – my door, the opposite-to-the-corridor one, was on the outside of the curve. Evidently the gendarmes had decided to stay in the corridor and enjoy the scenery on that side, probably thinking that they'd have plenty of time to arrest me and perhaps wanting actually to catch me using the camera. On my side the mountain and forest came right down to the track, which gave me the advantage. This was my chance. I didn't delay. I grabbed my suitcase and slung my camera round my neck while the gendarmes were still enjoying the scenery, opened the door as quietly as I could, and stood on the running-board. Then I pushed the door to just enough for the lock to catch without making a noise, threw my suitcase down, and jumped.

'It wasn't a very comfortable experience, I must say. Although the train had slowed down a good deal it must still have been doing between twenty and thirty miles an hour; and although I say I stood on the "running-board" I'm sure you'll appreciate that I was crouching and clinging rather than standing, with the door trying to slam in the airstream and great clouds of sooty smoke billowing down on me. It took me several seconds to get the door shut with one hand while I held on with the other; and by the time I jumped my suitcase was several hundred yards back down the line.

'I relaxed as I jumped, let myself roll over as I landed, and lay perfectly still. It was broad daylight and I should have been seen by other passengers if I'd stood up. After what seemed an eternity the rest of the train rattled past me, still rounding the mountain. I could see most of the inner curve of coaches and so far as I could detect there were no signs of alarm aboard. But of course I didn't know how long it would be before the gendarmes discovered my absence and stopped the train to search for me. I had to decide whether to travel up the wooded mountainside, follow the train north, or go back south. As my suitcase was back south my mind was partly made up for me. I walked back and retrieved it, feeling somewhat shaky and looking, I knew, dishevelled and grubby. But I didn't seem to have suffered any damage except a few grazes on the palms of my hands.

'There was no-one in sight. I had no idea where I was, but I began to tramp on southward. After a mile or so I arrived at a tiny country station. Klausen, it was called and it appeared to be completely deserted. But when I clambered up on to the platform and peered through the booking-office window I could see a solitary official poring over a ledger. At that moment the telephone beside him rang and I bobbed down out of sight, thinking it might be a call from the next station up the line telling him to be on the lookout for an escaped spy. But I had a fair knowledge of German and the call seemed to be about the re-timing of some goods train, so I relaxed again. When he'd finished his tele-phoning he saw me and came to the window and I asked him for a ticket to Bolzano. I'd decided that as the railway was the only means of transport and I had to continue my journey I'd best go back and start again. He produced the ticket and I put my hand in my pocket to pay for it. But – disaster number two for that day! – my wallet had gone. Either I'd left it behind at my Bolzano hotel or it had fallen from my pocket during my jump from the train. It had all my foreign currency and my tickets for the rest of the journey home in it, so I wasn't very happy about it. Fortunately, though, I always kept an English five-pound note and a golden sovereign in an inner secret pocket of my waistcoat and the clerk took the sovereign without any trouble at all. As I've said before, English money was always acceptable abroad in those days. But he didn't give me any change although the fare was only a few shillings, and I didn't want to make myself any more conspicuous than I was by arguing with him and perhaps having to explain how I came to be on this remote country station looking so dishevelled.

'There was an hour to wait for the next train back to Bolzano, and all the time I was in a sweat of apprehension wondering how soon the Innsbruck train would be stopped and a search party sent out. But nothing happened and eventually I arrived back at Bolzano, dashed straight round to my hotel, and asked the manager if my wallet had been found. It had – by the maid, who'd discovered it under my pillow when stripping the bed. I'd hardly expected to find such sterling honesty abroad, but I had the tact not to say so. I thanked him profusely, rewarded the maid, and caught the night train to Innsbruck. I was still apprehensive about pursuit and made myself as inconspicuous as possible. But nothing happened, and eventually I reached Innsbruck and got myself on to the Zürich train and away from the zone of suspicion, and that was the end of that adventure.'

As it happened it was also the end of our conversation for that day, for the Doctor had an appointment with a patient – one of two between whom I was sandwiched that afternoon –

and as I trotted off to catch my bus I reflected that his escape from arrest as a spy was just the kind of thing that John Buchan and a hundred other thickear adventure writers had woven into suspenseful dramas by heightening the effects. Forty-five miles an hour instead of twenty-five, gendarmes who were much quicker on the uptake than the real ones, a telephone call that was full of menace instead of goods-train schedules, and a pursuit up into the mountain over perilous chasms and round narrow ledges. Whatever else he was the Doctor was no story teller – either in the nursery or the literary senses. He left his narratives unadorned, a bit frayed at the edges and they were the better for it. I recalled the 'great clouds of sooty smoke billowing down' on him as he crouched on the running board; its acrid taste seemed to be in my mouth. I experienced the complete dislocation of all my bones as I thudded to the ground with him. I felt the cold manacles of a closing pursuit as I crouched by the booking-office window. By leaving all these sensations unremarked he had, I thought, heightened the effect of his 'touch of adventure'.

He had hinted darkly that his next anecdote might contain 'a touch of xenophobia' and I more or less expected something rather more powerful than the Victorian chauvinism expressed in his remark about having 'hardly expected to find such sterling honesty abroad'. It turned out, however, that what he felt strongly about was what he saw as the innate character of a particular race, not about foreigners in general.

As soon as I arrived he showed me a cutting from the *Sunday Times* of a week or two earlier. It carried an article entitled 'Overcoming the "inner pigdog" ' and pointed out that there had been a notable recurrence of duelling among students of West Berlin Free University since the ban imposed by the Allies after the war had been lifted by the Supreme Court in 1953. 'The vivid duelling scar down the cheek is once more in danger of becoming a passport to a good job in West Germany,' the writer said, 'and a guarantee that the owner of it is "a good German" . . . The duellists, who consider themselves the élite of the student movement, fight with three-foot swords, just under one inch wide and ground on both edges to razor sharpness to give deep cuts on the face. The right to belong to a fraternity is won by the ability to take the deep gashes without flinching while the blood from the wounds covers the floor. (A doctor is always in attendance to sew up the wounds or stop the contests if they are too severe.) In the strange language of the cult, such enforced stoicism is said to strengthen the character by "overcoming the inner pigdog".'

'I'm disgusted to learn this,' the Doctor said. 'It's particularly significant to me because of an experience I'm going to tell you about, belonging to an earlier year than that photographic adventure I mentioned last time. Nineteen-o-nine I think it was.' Although not exactly in a high pressure rage, he was more agitated than I'd seen him before and kept thrusting a forefinger at the cutting as if he'd taken deep personal affront at what he'd read there. 'This can mean only one thing: the Nazi spirit is stalking around again. Those people in England who are responsible for rearming Germany must be crazy. The simple, stark meaning of that phrase "overcoming the inner pigdog" is that the avenging war spirit, which is second nature to the German race, is being fostered in exactly the best breeding ground – the universities. The less bloodthirsty majority won't stay less bloodthirsty for long. As we all know from Hitler, there's no one more willing than the Germans to absorb ideas that suggest they're bigger and better than anyone else.' He put the cutting down in front of me and rang the bell for Veronica. When she came he asked her if she'd be so good as to bring the album she'd find in his car. 'I wanted you to see this,' he said to me, 'because it's got some pictures in it that confirm that sentence there about the right to belong to a fraternity being won by the unflinching way the duellists drip blood all over the floor while they wait for the doctors to stitch up their wounds. Ridiculous creatures! Clearly nothing at all has changed from my day.'

Presently Veronica returned and handed the Doctor a big scrapbook filled with press cuttings, photographs, theatre programmes, and other souvenirs. Riffling through the leaves he came upon what he wanted and handed the book to me. There were a dozen or so coloured postcards all belonging to a series collectively entitled *Mensur* (that is, Duelling) and showing young men wearing waxed moustaches and different amounts of padded clothing all fighting fiercely with swords of varying degrees of wickedness. Apparently the series illustrated a progression of different types of duel. In the first picture the duellists were padded up to their necks and had their eyes protected, but the rest showed them stripped of more and more protection until in the sixth they were fighting stripped to the waist. The remainder showed duellists sluiced in blood being bandaged and stitched by bloody-smocked doctors. Some attempt to express comic anguish had been made by some of the artists, but their main task seemed to have been to show plenty of blood. It dripped from the duellists' heads, faces, legs, and bodies into buckets and dishes on the floor; and the doctors were covered in it.

'You see?' the Doctor said. 'They take an absolute delight in it.' He went on to explain the six categories of duel. In the first grade, which is fought by freshmen over some trumped-up minor insult, the eyes and entire body are protected, while in subsequent grades the degree of protection becomes less and the justifying insult grows more heinous. The first five grades are fought with straight swords and only slashing downward is allowed – no thrusting or jabbing. But in the sixth grade curved cavalry sabres are used and thrusting, parrying, and feinting as in boxing are permissible; also, this super duel is preceded by a soap opera performance by a master of ceremonies who reads from a long scroll a Latin peroration giving details of the incident the parties are duelling about and appealing to them to settle their differences without recourse to a bloody battle from which maiming or death might result – an appeal that no one expects to be taken seriously.

'I saw one of these duels once,' the Doctor said. 'It was a deadly affair, held in a big wooden barn which was reached by an underground passage from an adjoining inn. A space about the size of a boxing ring had been cleared and this was surrounded by three tiers of benches. The students filled their beer mugs and crowded on to the benches, talking and smoking until the fight began. Once it was on there was a grim silence. The duellists circled the ring parrying and thrusting, for a time quite slowly and gracefully; then things quickened up and one of them was slashed along the arm. The blood flowed from a gash three or four inches long. Then the referee stopped the duel for a moment while the wound was sponged, after which it continued at a much faster pace. Suddenly I saw one duellist thrust his sabre into his opponent's chest just to the right of the breastbone; while it was still there the man whose chest was pierced brought his sabre down with terrible force on his adversary's head. It cleft a deep wound vertically down the forehead, cheek, and mouth, splitting both lips and the chin wide open. Both duellists fell to the ground and the one who had received the chest wound died in a few minutes. His opponent recovered – though of course he was terribly scarred for life – and shortly afterward "disappeared" to another university, which was the usual procedure in these wicked and senseless duels. No action was ever taken against a duellist who caused a death – he merely had to leave the university where it happened and continue his studies elsewhere. This was part of the unofficial encouragement given to what was officially a forbidden form of combat; and it was encouraged solely to stimulate the Germans' natural belligerence. The phrase "Der Tag" which we heard so much about in the Second World War was part of the students' common parlance even before the first one. They were moving even then toward "The Day" when they would be able to assert what they thought of as their racial superiority over the rest of Europe.

'But that's all by the way – background stuff. What I really set out to tell you was of an experience of my own when I was a student at Heidelberg University.

'There were no sports there – only the duelling on Saturdays and tramping on Sundays. The duelling disgusted me, so I worked off my surplus energy by going for long walks and hill climbs with two German students. They were pleasant companions and helped me with my German while I helped them with their Latin. One Sunday we'd had a particularly arduous tramp through the woods for many miles and when we got back to Heidelberg we were hot, dusty, tired, and thirsty. We all sat down at a table at an open-air café and ordered drinks. I've forgotten what they were, but mine was most probably ginger beer. I only remember that when it came it was in a stone bottle with a tricky cap that was raised by a lever on the side. I wasn't familiar with this kind of bottle, so didn't take very much care with the opening of it, and, to my embarrassment, the fizzy stuff escaped in hissing jets like champagne and spurted over my shoulder on to the head of a burly Prussian who was sitting at the next table with a girl. Naturally I immediately got up, apologized as best I could in my rather imperfect German, and offered him my handkerchief to mop his head with. He ignored both my apology and my handkerchief and, as I sat down again, rose and stood to attention before one of my companions with a click of heels and presented his card. Then he repeated the ceremony before my other chum and strutted off, taking his girl with him. My companions fell into a horrified silence and broke this only to tell me that I had been challenged to a duel on the following Saturday between six a.m. and noon. They had recognized the challenger as a notorious bully at the university and a notable duellist with both swords and pistols. Not only that, but the offence for which he had challenged me was practically the top offence of all: he'd been accompanied by a woman and imagined he'd been made to look ridiculous in her eyes. Nothing less than the sixth degree of duel would satisfy honour; and of course my friends had to act as my seconds. They had to meet my challenger's seconds daily before breakfast until each side had agreed on the terms of reference for the duel. They met on Monday and again on Tuesday, and then I was told that a very important concession had been gained on my behalf : I was to be allowed the choice of weapons. Well, since I knew nothing at all about either swords or pistols but did know quite a bit about boxing I naturally chose to fight with the fists. So my seconds declared my decision. And that really made the other side sit up. There were emergency meetings of both sets of seconds and general consternation. The other side ridiculed my choice and said that a fight with fists had never been fought in the history of the university. But as I'd been given the choice there wasn't much they could do about it except convey my decision to the challenger. This they did when they met for the fourth time on the Thursday morning; and by Friday the fight was off. My challenger's seconds coldly declared that there was nothing more to be said or done. I was, they added, a mad Englishman, only fit to be ignored. And as you may imagine, that was a decision I was perfectly happy with.'

Recalling his eminently sensible decision to use the advantage gained by his seconds in the best way, the Doctor laughed. 'I may be mad, but at least I'm not dead – which I might have been if I'd become involved in that barbarous duelling the Germans are so enamoured of. And then I'd never have had all these much more useful battles with my enemy.'

I told the Doctor it was now time I knew something about how he came to specialize in venereology, but he sharply reminded me that I didn't yet know how he had become a doctor – 'Not that that's a wildly exciting story, but I daresay you'd better have it for the record. Otherwise your readers are going to point out that here I am one minute squirting ginger beer over bull-headed Prussians' heads, and the next I'm concerned with a highly specialized branch of medicine in which there are even today relatively few practitioners.'

I agreed that this seemed an orderly notion and he went on to tell me how, as a youth completing his general education at Heidelberg, he had no leaning toward any particular calling. His father had told him that he could choose whatever profession he liked and that there was no hurry to make up his mind. 'You must be very sure,' he said, 'and having made your decision you must stick to it.' He was a typical Victorian, and haste in important decisions seemed foolish and unnecessary to him. Like many of his contemporaries he contrived to get an enormous amount of work done and at the same time lead a rich and full life with plenty of leisure for reflection and enjoyment. The only suggestion he made to his son was that as he was soundly grounded in Latin and Greek ('As a consequence of my diligence in making you learn them properly') and had in addition an excellent command of French and German, he might like to consider a professorship of languages. But that idea didn't appeal at all. 'Fluent though I was, I didn't fancy poring over the lexicons or mastering the cabalistic mysteries of foreign alphabets. Such a life seemed to me to promise boredom and monotony. I could never have sat for hours construing passages in other tongues. I felt the need of something more active. I'd had my fill of book learning and examinations, for I'd worked really hard at Heidelberg. Not that it had been necessary, for you could get away with anything at those German universities. You simply attended at the Dean's study during the first week of each term, paid your dues and had the attendance book signed. So far as the authorities were concerned you could then leave the room and not turn up again till the beginning of the next term if you felt so inclined. There were no compulsory examinations nor was attendance at lectures enforced. But my upbringing had tended to make me conscientious, and although many of my companions thought me pi I took it that my father had sent me there to study and study I did. In fact I was heartily sick of studying. So any job that involved more book learning had no appeal for me at all. I thought of sport, which I was very fond of, but that didn't seem to offer much aesthetic satisfaction. The law and the church would necessitate the additional study I wanted to avoid. Even the little I had seen of German militarism had put me right off the army. Photography didn't seem to offer much future as a profession. For the time being I was stymied. But as there was no immediate hurry I didn't bother much. And as so often happens when you stop bothering, the solution came up without any effort on my part.'

He rose and went through to an adjoining room and returned in a moment with what was apparently a small framed picture. This he held face down while he resumed his tale.

'The solution wasn't at all startling or dramatic. It came in the guise of five words which weren't at all dramatic either. But I'm not the only man whose life has been determined by overhearing a flat sentence that was spoken without any meaningful intent.'

He went on to explain how, during the days when he was considering what to do with his life, his sister was taken ill. It wasn't apparently a serious illness, but the family doctor was called in.

'It was quite by chance that I was passing my sister's bed-room door and heard the doctor talking to my parents about Charlotte's illness. He couldn't diagnose it properly and he was saying that it was very difficult in illnesses of this kind. (I don't think I ever discovered what it was, which is odd considering the effect it had on me; but she recovered from it, anyway.) And then he spoke the fatal words.'

The Doctor turned the frame uppermost with a little dramatic flourish and I saw now that it held, not a picture but a phrase of five words written in Italianate calligraphy :

> No Two Cases Are Alike

'It amused me to capture those words and pin them up in front of me like a Victorian "God Bless Our Home". There's really nothing remarkable about them, I'm sure you'll agree. They're words any doctor might have said and probably hundreds have. But they set me thinking. "If no two cases are alike," I thought, "how do doctors establish what is wrong?" I realized the phrase was just a figure of speech, that people's illnesses were diagnosed and cured, and that our doctor was just express-ing his mystification with a particular case. But it opened up wide avenues of thought : illness was something to investigate, you had to bring determination to your probings, back them up with a specialized knowledge so that you could solve an intricate problem and make a sick person well again. The pursuit of that knowledge suddenly appeared to me as exciting, a chase, a really worthwhile chase. I pondered on it a bit and a few days later I told my father that although I was utterly sick of books and examinations I'd decided to become a doctor. I had other misgivings about my choice besides my aversion from books and examinations: for one thing I couldn't bear to read or talk about blood, purulent discharges, or any other unpleasant manifestations of illness and I wondered if I'd be able to overcome this squeamishness. My father was a man of the opposite temperament – at my birth he'd delivered me himself because the doctor didn't arrive in time – but he didn't ridicule me. He assured me that the training I'd get in hospital would cure me of my frailty and that there was no point in wavering on that account. He told me to write off to the half dozen teaching hospitals in London for their prospectuses and make my choice. When the prospectuses came I pored over them with all the enthusiasm I'd given to Gamages' catalogue as a boy. I chose the one I knew had the best football team, but in the end my father convinced me that this wasn't a very good reason for choosing a hospital to learn my profession at and suggested I might think again. In the end I chose – well, you'll have to disguise it behind one of your pseudonyms, I suppose, but it was the one my father believed had the best teaching record judged by examination results. And because London University offered more challenging examinations than either Oxford or Cambridge I was enrolled there to work for my degree. It's strange how the horror I'd felt at the thought of more study and examinations had changed to enthusiasm because I'd decided to take up doctoring, but that's how it was.'

So there was the embryo doctor, a young man, ready to face another five years of gruelling study solely on the challenge of a five-word phrase that had aroused his curiosity. And a couple of days later, accompanied by his father, he presented himself for enrolment to the Secretary of the hospital I'm going to call here St Martin's. It was early September and the term started on the following day. 'You'll want some digs,' the Secretary said, 'and we have a list of recommended places. You'll find they don't vary much as to price and they're all in the immediate neighbourhood. Be here at nine sharp in the morning and you'll be allotted your working bench and timetable and Professor Mackinson will give you your introductory talk. After that you'll have very little spare time. You'll find yourself working till six here and continuing till midnight at your digs. Don't say you weren't forewarned. Medicine isn't a dilettante pursuit.'

'I'm glad to say I'd never thought it was,' the Doctor told me with a hint of the indignation he had felt at that observation by the Secretary. He ruminated for a moment, orientating himself back into that long distant day, perhaps trying to put into words his reaction at viewing, as through a reversed telescope, the minute beginning of his career. But he didn't come across with his reaction, whatever it may have been. Instead he told me how he and his father spent the rest of that day systematically working through the list of lodging house addresses they had been given. They decided with joint approval on a large airy room at the top of a biggish house in a residential road that had seen better times but was by no means squalid. The room cost £1 a week including a morning and evening meal and use of the bathroom – 'which had a fearsome but efficient gas geyser for heating water' – and a week's rent in advance was paid so that the embryo doctor could move in at once. The landlady was a sturdy Londoner who had married an Italian restaurateur and acquired the name of Poldini. She proved to be homely and kind, fed him huge meals to keep his strength up, and never minded him burning the gaslight until the early hours of the morning as he swotted over his books. The early part of any medical student's training is concerned largely with chemistry, botany, histology, zoology, and physiology, all of which are sciences that form the foundation on which the edifice of medicine is built. There can be no comprehension of disease or anatomy without a complete exploration of that foundation. The reading involved is complex and necessitates intense concentration, and for this reason the Doctor knew nothing about the life that went on in the rest of Mrs Poldini's house. He was dimly aware that there were other lodgers in the house, for sometimes he heard faint voices and people walking up and down the stairs. But none of this concerned him and it certainly wasn't audible enough to bother him while he worked at his books and examinations. He stayed there for a year and then moved to other digs which were slightly more expensive but had two rooms, so that he was able to share the expense with another student. When he gave Mrs Poldini notice she told him she was sorry to lose him and asked him if he would like to round off his stay by being a guest for dinner at her husband's restaurant in Soho. He accepted gladly, squeezing a single evening of relaxation from the unbroken term of study he had just completed, and enjoyed his dinner very much.

'Mr Poldini joined his wife and me for the meal and was most generous with the food and wine. He was a thin dark man with an olive skin and bald head, I remember, and during the third or fourth course the wine began to loosen his tongue. He became garrulous in an amusingly confidential way, leaning close to me but speaking loudly enough to be heard several tables away, much to the embarrassment of Mrs P., who kept trying to divert him from his revelations by making observations about the décor and service and how they could be improved. Mr P. wasn't having any diversion, however. He told me in an elaborately effusive way – which I believe he thought was very subtle and which was in fact so wrapped in winks and proddings that I found it hard to follow – that he and his wife were doing very well for themselves and had in fact established a couple of goldmines in the restaurant and the house. "They coincide together, you understand?" he kept saying. "The one takes on the fooding of the other. It is all most eminent, most complete. The ladies at the house make their gentlemen to bring them here for dinner, and the gentlemen here who ask Where are the ladies?

I send them to the house, you understand. It is all most eminent, a piece of building like a bridge, with one thing, one strut, depending on another and the whole making an eminent and dependable work that will support the weight of Signora Poldini and my own self as well, and this is a good comfort, you understand?" I scarcely did,' the Doctor continued after mimicking, with demonstrative flourishes, the heart of the garrulous Mr Poldini's revelation. 'Neither my parents nor anyone else had ever told me anything about sexual matters and even if I hadn't been working so hard I should have been scared of girls and shunned them. And even though I was a fully fledged medical student I had never heard of the so-called "social" diseases. So it took me a little time to absorb Mr Poldini's confidence. But when at last I'd pieced together my scraps of knowledge that were based mostly on my fellow students' references to copulation and whores, and held them against Mr Poldini's words, I arrived at the conclusion that my scrupulous father and the equally scrupulous Secretary of St Martin's had unwittingly had me living in a brothel. I was much amused.'

The Doctor's five years of training and study proved that his choice had been right. His interest in surgery and medicine never flagged. His only recreation was football, and he was secretary and captain of his hospital's team, in which he played full-back. He was one of a university soccer team that went to Moscow by invitation to play the then equivalent of the Russian Dynamos, and the official record of that visit has it that at Kalisz, on the Russo-Polish border, the whole team was disembarked from the train and delayed for a day while some question of invalid passports was settled. 'Eventually the party moved on,' the record says, 'in what today would be regarded as appalling conditions, on a hot, stuffy train which was devoid of drinking water long before it got to Moscow two days later. The slow travel was caused, apparently, by the large gaps left between the [ends of the] rails because of the temperature extremes experienced during the course of a year – more than twenty miles an hour being regarded as dangerous. The train stopped frequently and everyone disembarked for snacks at the trackside, with a three-bell warning of departure which was unheeded for the first two bells, but on the third everyone rushed madly to recover their places on the train.' The Doctor may well have had cause for extra alarm when the frontier guards brought their delaying tactics to bear, for he had taken his camera with him in spite of the strict rule against photography. It was in a leather case that looked very much like an ordinary attaché case, however, and no suspicion fell on him at that time. ('Later, though, I must have been spotted photographing in Moscow, for I was tailed all the way back to the frontier and might easily have become an international incident if they'd caught me using the camera again.') The sight-seeing tour laid on for the team in Moscow included the Kremlin, the famous Yar Restaurant where the dancing girls performed on mirrored floors and tables, and the Bolshoi Theatre. The London players won all their scheduled matches and were subsequently entertained in the Kremlin to a dinner followed by typically undergraduate high jinks which included tossing of the teams in carpets.

'That sort of break was very much of a rarity,' the Doctor said as he foraged about for, and eventually produced, photographs of the University team. 'In fact so far as I was concerned it was unique. Permission had to be granted by the Principal of the University and practically everyone else. It was of course far worse than getting clearance to play in a routine match involving a single afternoon – though that was no easy matter, and if you had any kind of duty to perform it was impossible even if you produced a hundred willing substitutes to take your duty for you. There were – and are – ways of circumventing regulations of course, and I took them as often as anybody else. But what you quickly realize is that every moment spent in recreation is a moment less to study in. And the curriculum for a medical student is a tough one: five years is scarcely a big enough frame to fit a huge picture into. For example, one speaks loosely of the study of anatomy; but this in itself is a big subject and isn't, as so many non-medical people seem to think, confined to learning the functions of the bones and organs of the human body. There's morphology, which is comparative anatomy and deals with the structure of animal and plant forms under the sub-divisional headings of zootomy and phytotomy. And human anatomy itself sub-divides into several complex studies. Embryology deals with pre-natal development, histology with the structure of the tissues, cytology with the structure of the cells that form the tissues. Then there's onotogeny, which is the study of the characteristic changes in the individual, and phylogeny, the study of the changes characteristic of a species. The human skeleton alone demands three distinct anatomical studies – osteology, the bones; myology, the muscles; and arthrology, the joints. And the organs inside it demand three more – splanchnology, the viscera; angiology, the blood vessels, and neurology, the brain and nerves. Even when you've got a grasp of these – which are called collectively systematic anatomy – you have to add applied anatomy and its four sub-divisions, medical anatomy, surgical anatomy, surface anatomy, and X-ray anatomy.'

The Doctor paused in his recapitulation of the medical student's mammoth tasks and refreshed himself with a cup of Veronica's tea, which had just arrived. But before he had taken half a dozen sips he was away again.

'Then chemistry. This is another complex study with two main branches – organic chemistry and inorganic chemistry. Put in plain language, organic chemistry is concerned with determining the molecular structure of natural and synthetic carbon compounds – which means in effect all living or organized matter, for all living matter contains the element of carbon. Inorganic chemistry, as you can guess if you didn't already know, is the study of the chemical properties of the elements other than carbon and their division into what are called "atomic numbers". The atomic number of Hydrogen is One, and of

Radium, Eighty-eight, and between those there are another eighty-six elements you have to know about. Mercury, which later proved to have a special reference to my particular study, is number Eighty, and Bismuth – also very important to the venereologist – is number Four; but that's by the way. All I want to get over to you is that those five years have to be carefully spent – they're not a moment too long.'

My head reeling slightly at the thought of so many 'ologies' and 'otomies' and atomic numbers, I told the Doctor he'd got it over to me with some success, and that a mere manipulator of words, who has a lifetime to spend on his manipulations and at the end of it is unlikely to have enriched humanity with any of them and even more unlikely to have earned any human gratitude, could only bow the head in dumb wonder.

'Well it's not all that wondrous,' he said briskly. 'Lots of people do it : you've only got to look at the Medical Directory – it's practically as thick as Who's Who. I did it all right in five years, getting my two qualifying degrees without trouble. These were M.R.C.S. and L.R.C.P., which meant, in the full panoply of their significance, that I'd become a Member of the Royal College of Surgeons and a Licentiate of the Royal College of Physicians. But in those days that didn't mean that you could just rent a house somewhere and put your plate on the door : it meant that you waited for some hospital appointment to become vacant, applied for it along with dozens of other newly qualified chaps, and got it if you were lucky. I was lucky in getting three appointments at St Martin's. I was House Surgeon for six happy months there, and Casualty Officer and Resident Anaesthetist, with the additional job of Clinical Assistant in the Ear, Nose and Throat department thrown in, at the end of that year and the beginning of the next one. These appointments meant that I was gaining wide experience; and at the end of it I'd decided that I was going to specialize in surgery. My father, of course, proved to be right when he told me I should quickly overcome my queasiness at the sight of blood and other unpleasant manifestations of illness. I could gaze at the

most dreadful sights with equanimity. And if you're Casualty
Officer in a big hospital you don't get spared much. But it's
surprising how shocking some injuries – such as those sustained
in street accidents – can look yet at the same time be of minor
severity. Bone and tissue in the human body are of astonishing
durability when it comes to external batterings. It's the little
disease germs that are their ruination – and, of course, there are
other things, such as mental illness, that are pitiable in the extreme and in their way much more terrifying than gashes,
abrasions, and broken bones.'

He went on to explain how, as a student at St Martin's, the
study of mental diseases had been part of his curriculum, with
the old London insane asylum, St Mary of Bethlehem (popularly called Bedlam and now turned into the Imperial War
Museum) as the venue for investigation. There, there had been
one case in particular that had remained in his memory for no
other reason than that it was the most ordinary of delusionary
cases (the ordinary can often be as memorable as the
remarkable).

'He was a neat, middle-aged man with a small goatee beard,
very clean and fresh looking, and he used to sit all day long at
the open window, tapping the ledge as he peered out through
the trees on to the street below. When I asked him to tell me
what he was at, he very gently and politely replied that he understood my ignorance and would enlighten me. He looked hastily
round the room to make sure we were not overheard, then told
me confidentially that he was God. "I run the universe from
this window," he said. "Look down in the street, now, and see
how when I tap my fingers on the window-ledge the trams move
up and down. You see? There goes one now – and another in
the opposite direction. You see how smooth it all is? That is
because I am very experienced. I have been running the universe
for a very long time now, and it runs very well." I was touched
by this man's odd activity: it was innocent enough and it seemed
to give him pleasure. Yet a disturbed mind such as his seemed a
sinister and terrible thing, I imagined its balance being upset

to a further minuscule extent so that instead of sitting there all day benevolently playing the part of God he ran berserk with a wild look in his eyes, laying about him with an iron bar, killing with terrible fury every creature in his path. And that extra small disturbance was easily possible. I remember being so moved by the case that I asked Professor Elmore Paynton, who was the specialist accompanying us, if anything was known of the cause of this man's derangement. "Oh yes," he said, "syphilis. He's a G.P.I." Well, by that time I was an advanced student and knew something about venereal disease and general paralysis of the insane. But it was the effect on that particular individual – that nice chap with his pink cheeks and little beard – rather than the cause, that I remembered for some time to come. He haunted me a bit; and, as things turned out, to good purpose.'

Suddenly the Doctor jumped up, polished his reading glasses, and went to refer to his appointments diary. 'But I can't stop to tell you about that now. I've a patient due in five minutes – a girl who's foolishly relied on some back-street quack for treatment for syphilis, but her history sheet shows she hasn't done herself much good. So if you'll forgive me . . .?'

I departed at once, leaving the Doctor to wrench his mind from the past to the present and more important matters than mine. On second thoughts, though, I doubt whether much of a wrench was involved.

# 8   A Sword for the Battle

The Book of Leviticus, which is a book of rules of social and
moral behaviour written by priestly scribes of the tribe of Levi,
prescribes (in Chapter Fifteen) instructions for the treatment
of gonorrhoea. The prescription is limited to washing the
infected parts with water, which couldn't have been very
effective but wouldn't have done any harm. (Soap, which is a
combination of animal or vegetable fat with soda or potash,
didn't make its appearance as a cleansing agent until, at the
earliest, the first century, A.D. Leviticus was written about 400
B.C.) Other instructors and instruction books, both before and
after the Levites' time, have stumbled on better and worse treatments. The origins of all physical illnesses except wounds caused
by violence, as in hunting or battle, were unknown until in 1683
the Dutch microscopist Antoni van Leeuwenhoek established the
existence of minute malignant organisms – bacteria – that used
the human system as a venue for battle against the benign
organisms inherent there, and sometimes overcame them, thus
causing disease. And until something of this main cause of infection was known all medical treatment was necessarily by hit-or-
miss methods. Even hit-or-miss methods are occasionally
successful, however, and the gradual accumulation of experience
– which doctors painstakingly recorded after the first medical
treatise in history, the *Hippocratic Corpus*, had been published
in the third century B.C. – formed the single edge of the therapeutic sword with which the battle against disease was fought.
By discovering the existence of bacteria Leeuwenhoek sharpened
the second edge of the sword, and his successors have wielded it
with increasing effect.

The venereal diseases, as I've explained, were for centuries confused with diseases with superficially similar manifestations such as yaws, smallpox, and leprosy, and such treatment as was going was applied to all of them. It was logical to assume that the surgical opening of swellings would let the causal poisons escape; and equally logical schools of thought maintained that the application of ointments and salves or the swallowing of medicine killed the illness within, or that induced excessive sweating forced it out. In the case of venereal swellings, of course, the surgeon's course was obvious: he simply cut them open. And sweat-baths posed no great problem either. The Greek historian Herodotus, who lived in the fifth century B.C., describes those used by the Scythians: 'They make tents with three poles meeting at the top covered with felt, and having enclosed them as well as they can, they heat stones in a fire until they glow, and throw them in a vessel in the middle of the tent. They had a wild hemp in their country, like flax except that it grows taller and stouter by far. They take the seed of this hemp, and creeping under the felt covering of the tent they throw the seed on the stones glowing with heat from the fire, and there it smoulders and makes such a steam as no vapour-bath in Greece could surpass, and the steam makes the Scythians howl for joy.' No doubt these howling Scythians were for the most part merely cleansing their bodies in their steamy wigwams; but the medicinal effect of steam is noted by many Greek and Roman physicians, who prescribed the sweat-bath willy-nilly as an initial treatment for any illness they couldn't diagnose – much as fashionable but incompetent Victorian physicians prescribed 'a change of scene' for patients who were rich, bored, and overfed. After venereal diseases had been established as such – and even after the difference between syphilis and gonorrhoea was known; in fact well into the nineteenth century – sweat-baths were part of the recognized treatment. They were simple to fabricate, had a suitably punishing effect on the patient's body and conscience, and were often harshly effective in expelling the germs with the sweat. (Sometimes they expelled the patient's life too, for complete dehydration of a human body is fatal.) But when it came to treatment with ointments and medicines the way was thrown wide open for quackery as well as genuine experiment, for ointments and medicines may contain virtually anything, and patients (or the loved ones of patients) in despair are the easiest of game for the charlatan. There wouldn't be any point in cataloguing all the 'remedies' the quacks have swindled their patients with in the history of venereal diseases. But most of them were useless and some of them – for example the burning out of syphilitic sores with sulphuric acid – positively harmful. If their nostrums were inspired by anything other than avarice it was more likely to have been superstition than medical experience. The mysterious causes of illness have always spatchcocked neatly into the mysterious cures of superstition; and even the advances of science have left a great many people listening to the screwy tales of old wives.

To state accurately whether the knife, the sweat-bath, ointment, or medicine was the first to be used to cure venereal diseases is impossible. For centuries no causal difference between venereal and other diseases characterized by rashes, pocks, and swellings was known, and it seems likely that the earliest efforts at curing all of them might have been made with ointment, for sores and discharges invite treatment by inunction. The earliest ointments were compounded of herbs and fats and are unlikely to have had much effect. Trial and error, however, eventually arrived (in the first century, A.D.) at a combination of sandalwood oil and potash, which is soap. Soap hasn't any curative properties, but as a cleansing agent it no doubt limited the epidemic effects of gonorrhoea, for *Neisseria gonorrhœae* is allergic to it – and to heat too, so that clothes left lying in the sun to dry after being washed with soap and water are not contagious. The advice in Leviticus about the constant washing of clothes, flesh, and bed linen became doubly effective once soap was invented.

The first ointment with directly curative power in the venereal diseases was made from mercury, which was introduced into medicine by the Chinese, who noticed that the crystallized ore of mercury, cinnabar, disintegrates when it's heated and releases mercuric vapour. The vapour can either be inhaled or allowed to condense in a cold jar and then mixed with fat to make ointment. Arabian traders brought it from the east and sold it in Africa and Europe as a remedy for all diseases characterized by skin eruptions. And although the confusion between the different diseases was then complete, it was soon found that mercury ointment has a healing effect on some of them – including the one we now know as syphilis. So an advance had been made not only toward cure but toward differentiation too.

Mercury has remained one of the principal specifics in the treatment of syphilis ever since. Apart from the sweat-bath and surgery it was in fact the only true specific available until the twentieth century. (Iodine too was used in the nineteenth century, but its effect was mainly to stimulate and restore damaged tissues.)

The oldest successful method of administering mercury is of course as an ointment; but in the early years of the sixteenth century, when the so-called Columbian epidemic of syphilis was ravaging Europe and desperate attempts were being made to find a cure, the doctors elaborated the old Chinese method of inhalation. Their elaborations were the death of many of their patients, for they weren't content to let the patients inhale the mercurial fumes by smoking pipes as the Chinese did – a method that ensured the inhalation of fresh air as well as fumes. They mixed the mercury with other poisonous substances – for example, sulphur, red lead oxide, and volatilized calomel (which gives off fumes of hydrochloric acid) – and preceded the inhalations by purging, bleeding, and sweating. If the patient survived this he was stripped naked and put in a Scythian tent until he was almost asphyxiated by mercurial fumes. Understandably, the treatment wasn't popular. It was, however, often effective because the lungs absorb mercury easily and pass it into the system by way of the respiratory tract. Success depended mainly on whether the patient's lungs could stand up to the irritation. Modern doctors seem to belittle the value of treatment by inhalation. They have also for the most part discarded treatment by mercury in tablet form – another very popular method of administering it during and after the sixteenth century. This is because cumulative doses of mercury are needed to attack the venereal organisms in the body but only small doses can be given by ingestion because the poison irritates the stomach and intestine. (This is why mercurial preparations should be taken only after meals.)

The modern way of giving mercurial treatment is by injection. The salts of the drug can be injected into the muscles or into the tissues beneath the layer of fat under the skin. Nobody cares to use that subcutaneous method much because it's very painful and causes abscesses. Intra-muscular injection is less painful but may cause the formation of nodes (inflamed swellings) or lead to bronchopneumonia or haemorrhage.

As you see, treatment by mercury was somewhat uncertain of success and had many disadvantages. That much I had grasped from my reading of many thousands of words in medical tomes. The tomes were heavy in both senses of the word, and their revelations were larded with jargon, chemical formulae, and other obscurities. But I felt knowledgeable enough to ask the Doctor which, if any, mercurial treatment he'd use – and why. Armed with a briefcase stuffed with notes and chanting softly to myself, 'Inunction, inhalation, ingestion, injection; intramuscular, intravenous, subcutaneous' I visited him one rainy day in November. By now I had registered in my mind so many photographs of venereal lesions that I habitually glanced with furtive curiosity at the legs of the woman ahead of me on the escalator, at the eyes of the man opposite me in the bus, or the hands of the barmaid pouring my Scotch. My curiosity was partly compassionate but mostly, I fear, concerned with practising my supposed new ability to identify venereal signs. And on this day it was rewarded (though that's scarcely a kind word to use). Hurrying from the bus stop I encountered a man whose terrible face peered at me briefly through the rain. The nose itself had been almost entirely eaten away and the destruction

had spread to the cheeks, lips, and lower forehead. To avoid
inflicting his appearance on others he had masked himself with
a thin scarf; but this, sodden with the rain, had slipped and
momentarily revealed his pitiable condition. I felt shocked, but
I wouldn't deny that my horror was to a certain extent lessened
by my gratification at recognizing an undoubted case of syphilis.
It also occurred to me that probably hundreds of people without my small amount of accumulated specialized knowledge
might have had as little difficulty as I did in assuming the cause
of the man's condition. But I, I felt, was diagnosing rather than
assuming. I felt myself something of an expert in a small way.

Somewhat enthusiastically I told the Doctor of my encounter.
He chuckled amiably. 'I wouldn't care to have you as my
doctor,' he said. 'The condition you describe may well have
been syphilis. It might also have been several other things –
cancer, tuberculosis, scrofuloderma, epithelioma; in certain circumstances they may all be mistaken for syphilis. So may some
kinds of acne – acne rosacea, for example, and rhinophyma,
which is congestion of the blood vessels of the nose and cheeks,
popularly known as "grog blossom".' I suppose he noticed my
crestfallen look for he added: 'Well, don't worry about it. Proper
doctors have made the same mistake – not too often I hope.'

I took this to be a suitable moment to trip quietly out of the
glare of the spotlight, which I turned at once on to the proper
subject of my visit. The Doctor listened attentively to my questions about the circumstances in which he might use mercury
and his choice of method of administering it. Characteristically,
he then paused for several moments while he assembled in his
mind the answer that would be most helpful to me. During this
time he loped about the room referring to one or two books and
making notes on the back of an envelope. Then he said:

'You've put yourself at a bit of a disadvantage. You're in the
position of a doctor living before the nineteenth century, when
mercury was virtually the only treatment available. Since then
several different treatments have been discovered: bismuth; the
arsenobenzenes such as Salvarsan and its variations; the iodides;

the sulpha drugs; and of course penicillin. I've got the choice of all of them and know more or less all about all of them. Your knowledge is limited to mercury. I think you'd better extend it to include the others. Because your question about when I'd use mercury can be answered only if I can tell you when I'd use *them*.' He saw me shuffling my notes together and added: 'But don't go yet. There are other things we can talk about. Where did I get to in my personal history?'

I told him I'd left him in Bedlam, before he'd qualified at St Martin's watching a little bearded man with G.P.I. playing God.

'So it was. Well, I can tell you about another bearded man who crossed my path later the same year. That was Bernard Shaw, and I spent half an hour or so after I had been called out of bed on his behalf at 2 a.m. when I found it necessary to put three stitches into a cut on his head. That was after I'd qualified, of course, and was acting as Casualty Officer at St Martin's – a job that brought you into contact with absolutely everything that came into the Casualty Department. You got a wonderful variety of experience, though I must admit that on Saturday nights in those days it was a bit monotonous – nothing much but drunks who'd been beating each other up. You stitched and plastered them, stomach-pumped them, and turned 'em out again. There was seldom any variation on Saturday nights. Other times, though . . . well there were many mystifying things.'

Holding Bernard Shaw as it were by the index card for future reference, I followed the Doctor off down his own sidetrack.

'I remember once being confronted with a mother and her fretful child – a little girl who was covered from head to foot with a most alarming rash. I knew I'd have to go very carefully here. Something contagious, obviously, but I couldn't identify it. It hadn't the characteristics of any of the ordinary things like measles or chicken-pox or scarlet fever. I was so bothered about it that I summoned the physician on duty– I wasn't going to be responsible for letting the child go and starting some epidemic. He came – a bit disgruntled, as physicians often are when they're called to the Casualty Department – and looked at the child.

Then he looked at me, and he wasn't a bit more pleased. "Good God," he said, "haven't you ever seen those before? They're fleabites." '

Recollecting his gaffe, the Doctor smiled. 'I ought to have known really. That was a terribly crummy part of London. Some of the houses we had to go to on midwifery duty were filthy. We used to pour chloroform down our trousers and into our socks to act as a killer of bugs and body-lice. The amount of dirt and ignorance you found was astonishing – and this was in the second decade of the twentieth century. Women would wash themselves and the household's dirty linen once a week at the public wash-houses, and they'd take advantage of that visit to defecate too. That was the only time they cleared their bowels. You may remember that Somerset Maugham was a doctor in the eighteen-nineties; he quotes somewhere the Professor of Gynaecology who began his lecture by saying, "Gentlemen, woman is an animal that micturates once a day, defecates once a week, menstruates once a month, parturates once a year, and copulates whenever she has the opportunity." Well, that was literally true in every respect of a good many of the London women I got to know at St Martin's. They were wonderful characters, but sometimes astonishingly ignorant. I remember one who came to be examined : I couldn't find anything wrong with her at all, and I couldn't get any sense out of her. She had no pains, no symptoms, and as it's not good practice to ask leading questions I was mystified. Eventually I asked her why she'd come at all. "Why, because I'm ill," she said. "I *must* be ill, because I've been married thirteen years and every year for twelve years I've had a baby. Now this year, no baby. I *must* be ill." '

Splendidly in his stride now, the Doctor rattled on. 'Ignorance in sexual matters was, and still is, astonishing. Everybody laughs at the classic story of the married couple who thought they were copulating merely by rubbing their navels together; but I've known lots of couples to whom it actually happened. In one case this curious arrangement replaced natural coitus for eight years before the couple came to the hospital for advice. These people aren't mentally deficient or physically deformed or under-developed: it's simply that the idea that babies emerge from the navel has, to them, a natural corollary – which is that the navels must be rubbed together in the first place, like Aladdin's lamp or something. And that notion has become an *idée fixe* which has completely defeated natural instinct. There were others who hadn't even got an *idée fixe*: they simply had no notion at all. One girl came to me once, I remember, and told me she was getting married and would like to know "what was expected" of her. I told her to leave that to her husband. "Don't worry," I said, "he'll know what to do." "But he's waiting outside," she said. "He sent me in to find out." The Doctor laughed out loud at his merry memory, assured me that he had instructed the innocent husband in the normal method of copulation, then suddenly turned grave. 'But this kind of ignorance was at least harmless. There were other kinds that weren't. A particularly vicious belief used to be held – especially among Jewesses – that venereal disease could be cured by coitus with a virgin male. I recall that when I had to treat several boys who had acute gonorrhoea I was puzzled because they all gave addresses in the same street. When we went into things we found they'd all been enticed by the same whore, who also lived in that street. They were just children, schoolboys of thirteen and fourteen, and had been corrupted by this wretched woman who believed in this crackpot superstition. And there were God knows how many grown men and women who believed that both infection and conception could be prevented if you coughed and urinated directly after coitus. That ignorant belief led to more abortions and venereal infections than I'd care to try to count. I know it's a cliché, but it's true that doctors have to fight half their battles against disease and the other half against ignorance – just plain, shocking ignorance.'

Gently I led the Doctor back from his own by-way by suggest-ing that at least he wouldn't have found Bernard Shaw ignorant.

'Indeed I did; but ignorant in a different way – ignorant of

good manners. He walked into the Casualty Department with
a cut head and two of the worst punched-up eyes you ever saw.
I asked him how he got into that state – just conversationally,
you know, to take his mind off things while I was putting the
sutures in – and he told me he'd jumped off a moving bus and
run into a lamp-post. I ask you! As if I hadn't seen enough black
eyes in my time to know that he'd been in a fight. It was the
assurance with which he expected to be believed that made it so
insulting. Just because I was a junior doctor and he was an international figure he thought it right to fob me off with a stupid
story like that. As if I cared what fight he'd been in. It was
probably something to do with his anti-war opinions. He was
very unpopular, you know, between nineteen-fourteen and nineteen-eighteen, and I daresay he got beaten up at some meeting
he'd been addressing.' The Doctor shrugged Mr Shaw out of the
room into the rain. 'Never mind him. There's a booklet here – a
couple of chapters I wrote for a new edition of one of those big
books you're reading. It's on the diagnosis and treatment of
venereal diseases, and it'll enlighten you a bit in your studies.'

In the bus I glanced at the booklet and read: 'Medical Officers
are warned against a hasty declaration of venereal disease to the
patient before the clinical evidence has been confirmed by
positive pathological results, as such a diagnosis may lead to
serious legal and domestic consequences and proceedings may
be taken against the medical officer for a mistaken diagnosis.' A
pretty girl sitting next to me had glimpsed the bold black-type
heading: 'Of venereal diseases: Chapter XXIX: Syphilis.' She
looked horrified.

My researches into the post-mercurial discoveries in the
treatment of syphilis revealed that a new keenness was given to
the edge of the therapeutic sword by Paul Ehrlich, the German
chemist who shared the 1908 Nobel prize for medicine with the
Russian bacteriologist Elie Metchnikoff. Ehrlich was born in
1854 in Silesia, where his parents kept an inn called 'The Wreath
of Rue'. He qualified as a doctor but devoted almost his entire

working life to chemistry. His patience and thoroughness in research into the chemical structure of aniline dyes established that they had a curative effect on sleeping sickness, and Robert Koch, the German bacteriologist who had isolated the bacillus of tuberculosis, invited him to work at the Institute for Infectious Diseases. Subsequently he became Director of the State Institute for Serum Research, and, in 1906, of the German Royal Institute for Experimental Therapy at Frankfurt. There he conducted innumerable experiments in a search for synthetic chemical substances that would act destructively on malign organisms without poisoning the patient. In 1905 Schaudinn had established beyond all doubt that the causal germ of syphilis was *Spirochaeta pallida*, and Ehrlich chose syphilis to do battle with in his researches.

Ehrlich's secretary and biographer, Martha Marquardt, makes it clear that although he was benign, absent-minded, always surrounded in his Institute with immense fortifications of books – the personification of the stage professor – his mind was so quick to grasp explanations that he had absorbed what people were trying to tell him long before they'd finished speaking the actual words, and therefore let his thoughts wander freely on ahead. His powers of concentration were intense, and he had mastered a way of reading diagonally down the page in order to be able to read the maximum number of books in the minimum of time. He almost completely disregarded his own health, ate frugally and irregularly, and smoke-dried his inside with vicious black cigars. After suffering two strokes, he died in 1915.

Ehrlich's researches into a cure for syphilis were assisted by a young Japanese, Dr Hata, who had independently begun a series of experiments at the Kitasato Institute for Infectious Diseases in Tokio as soon as Schaudinn's discovery was announced in 1905. He had succeeded in infecting rabbits with syphilis while Ehrlich was similarly inoculating white mice and following the inoculations with hundreds of different substances in attempts to find a destructive agent for *Spirochaeta pallida*.

By 1907 Ehrlich had worked out six hundred and six variations of a formula based on atoxyl (arsanilic acid), which had been found efficacious in the treatment of sleeping sickness – the germs of which are called *Trypanosomes* and have, Schaudinn believed, a strong affinity with *Spirochaetes* in their chemotherapeutic reactions. Other chemists had tried atoxyl on syphilitically infected animals but had found that only doses repeated often enough to kill the animals as well as the *Spirochaeta* were effective. Ehrlich felt certain that atoxyl was the right basic drug, and his six hundred and six experiments were all concerned with reducing the toxicity to humans while maintaining the toxicity to *Spirochaeta pallida*. Chemically, his experiments bridge the gap between

AsO (OH)$_2$

NH$_2$

(which in plain language proves merely that atoxyl is the sodium salt of para-aminophenylarsonic acid) and

As ══════════ As

HCl    NH$_2$              NH$_2$    HCl

OH                    OH

(which is the end-product of Ehrlich's numerous attempts to change a molecular structure in which the chemical constituents had a benign influence on *Spirochaeta pallida* and a malign influence on the tissues of the body into one in which the exactly reverse effect obtained). The change was made by introducing organic arsenic into a combination of hydro-chloride (which is soluble in water) and dioxydiaminoarsenobenzol (which isn't). This compound was tried out on various animals, on two physicians named Hoppe and Wittneken, and on syphilitic idiots, and found to have no fatally toxic effects, though it had inflammatory effects on some cranial nerves. The compound was finally called arsphenamine and marketed under the trade name of

'Salvarsan 606'. It was announced to the medical world at the Congress for Internal Medicine at Wiesbaden on 19 April, 1910.

The delay between 1907, when Ehrlich originally patented arsphenamine, and 1910, when he announced it, was caused by inadequate trials conducted by one of his assistants, who told Ehrlich that it had no effect on syphilitic animals and that an earlier compound, arsenophenylglycin, was better. It was Dr Hata, whose patience was as inexhaustible as Ehrlich's own, who proved the contrary. When he arrived, Martha Marquardt records, he was given samples of both drugs (arsenophenylglycin was numbered 418, arsphenamine 606) and told to conduct long series of experiments. 'Having made his first experiments', she goes on, 'Dr Hata remarked: "Believe six-o-six *very* efficacious." Ehrlich looked at the records and said, much astonished: "No, surely not . . . it was all minutely tested by Doctor R, and *he* found nothing – nothing . . . More than a year ago we laid six-o-six aside as being ineffective, worthless. You are sure you are not mistaken, Doctor Hata?" Hata pointed to the records of his experiments and said, shrugging his shoulders: "I found *that*, Herr Direktor." "Then it must be repeated, dear Hata, repeated," said Ehrlich. "To be sure of what we find there must always be many – innumerable – controls and repetitions. That must be the basis of our work." He looked happily at Dr Hata, who bowed and left the room. Ehrlich walked up and down the room, talking to himself. "I always had a strong feeling – have been convinced for two years – *that six-o-six must be good!*" ' And so it proved when Dr Hata had conducted his 'many – innumerable – controls and repetitions'.

Arsphenamine was first administered by intramuscular injections and, like mercury, caused great pain and some necrosis of the tissues; but administered intravenously it was found to be painless, non-destructive to the tissues, and much more effective than mercury. For some patients, however, it had mildly toxic effects and Ehrlich went on with another three hundred experiments until, in 1912, he produced an improved form which he called neoarsphenamine and which was marketed as 'Neo-sal-varsan 914'. One or other of the basic formulae 606 and 914, varied occasionally by differences in quantity of the constituent elements, or by the addition of such metals as silver, remained the most effective treatment for syphilis until the discovery of penicillin in 1943.

But though in general 606 and 914 were the most effective they were challenged by two other important drugs in the nine-teen-twenties. These were sulpharsphenamine – which has a constitution differing from neoarsphenamine by the presence of one additional atom of oxygen, making it very easily soluble and suitable for intramuscular use – and bismuth.

Bismuth is a metallic element resembling arsenic and antimony chemically, and it can be given as a treatment for syphillis in four main forms – preparations of the metallic element itself, of its organic salts, its mineral salts, and its alkaloid derivatives. It was first used therapeutically in the eighteenth century, but nobody thought of using it against syphilis until another hun-dred years had passed, when it was tried out on syphilitically infected dogs and found to be fatally toxic – apparently because an ammonium citrate form was used. Then, in 1921, two medical scientists called Sazerac and Levaditi, discovered that in another form (tartrobismuthate of potassium and sodium) it had a definitely curative effect on syphilitic rabbits; and a year later two other patient researchers, Fournier and Guenot, con-firmed – by trials on two hundred human subjects – that in some cases it was even more effective than the arsenobenzene drugs, but was in any event an invaluable discovery in the treatment of syphilis.

All these drugs have remained in the therapeutic repertory of venerealogists; and so, to a very small extent, have a number of others – including the salts of various heavy metals such as tellurium, antimony, cadmium, gold, vanadium, and copper, and the vegetable substances guaiac, quinine and sarsparilla. But these have been found of use only in isolated cases and I mention them only for the record and to suggest the immense scope of the research that went into – and is still going into – the curing of syphilis. Any new line of approach must involve hundreds – sometimes thousands – of separate chemical experiments, and each of them must be followed to the point where the reactions of both the *Spirochaeta* and the patient are discovered.

Nature too has provided one form of treatment which has proved to be of some value, especially in cases of syphilis in its early stages : this is by immersion in thermal baths containing sulphur. Hot springs exist in many parts of the world – notably at Kusatsu in Japan, Arkansas, and Aachen – and patients whose intolerance to mercurial and arsenical drugs is high can often be helped in the elimination of the poison from their systems by the sulphur content of such springs. Even ordinary hot baths in hospital tubs are not without value in the treatment of gonorrhoea. In the case of gonorrhoea the warmth is helpful because it eases the irritation and reduces the discharge; but the reason for the occasional beneficial effect of hot baths on syphilis isn't precisely known. However, two doctors named Mehrtens and Pouppirt record that in 1927 they gave nine hundred baths to seventy syphilitic patients during a period of eighteen months. The baths were of a temperature of 110° F., lasted about an hour, and were followed by envelopment in blankets and maintenance of high temperatures with water-bottles and hot drinks. The patients included eleven in whom syphilis had caused partial paralysis, and of these two recovered completely and seven showed improvement. Clearly, balneotherapy isn't to be sneered at.

But all extant forms of treatment were put in the shade by the introduction, in 1935, of the sulphonamide drugs and, in 1943, of penicillin. Sulphanilamide, which is the sulphonamide drug most used, was found to have a very marked destructive effect on *Neisseria gonorrhoeae* but none at all on *Spirochaeta pallida*. But penicillin was an unfailing destroyer of both. In one of the many technical papers I found myself reading while tracing the history of post-mercurial treatment I came upon the following statement :

'That penicillin, the most highly selective anti-biotic known, should be able to exert its amazing lethal effect on two such widely differing pathogenic organisms as the gonococcus, a non-motile gram-negative bacterium, and the *Spirochaeta pallida,* a mobile spiral protozoon, is one of the most interesting facts of modern science. Sir Alexander Fleming's romantic discovery, the first therapeutic agent to be truly specific against both gonorrhoea and syphillis, has revolutionized the treatment and prognosis of these diseases. All the more so, because a therapeutic response occurs not only in the acute but also in the chronic stages of both infections. Penicillin is the best and most successful cure for gonorrhoea that has so far been discovered  . . [in early syphilis] the lesions heal promptly and the immediate spiro-chaeticidal effects are superior to those with arsenotherapy . . . [in congenital syphilis] the specific potency of penicillin and its comparative non-toxicity has provided us with an unsurpassed therapeutic power of inestimable value . . . [And in late syphilis] penicillin causes a rapid involution of syphilitic lesions . . . ulcerations of the leg and neck heal progressively within three to six months, while symptoms from active visceral gummata can disappear in a few days . . . Syphilis is a long-term recurrent disease and the end results cannot be properly assessed in the short time of four years. Enough is known, however, to show that penicillin is superior to any other anti-syphilitic drug, that the predictability of final cure remains the same as hitherto, and that it is dangerous to depend on penicillin alone to cure syphilis.'

Feeling that I'd now built up my background enough to question the Doctor again on his views on different treatments (and understand his answers) I presented myself once more at his door. Veronica led me into the waiting-room. 'The Doctor has a patient,' she said, 'but I don't think he'll be very long.' She handed me *Vogue,* the *Financial Times,* and the *Which?* report on contraceptives, and left me. Fascinated by *Which*'s discoveries of the uselessness of large numbers of contraceptives

I passed a happy half-hour. Then Veronica came to tell me the Doctor was ready for me and I went along the corridor to the consulting-room, still clutching the report.

He was in a garrulous mood and before I'd got my coat off and sat myself on the sofa had begun to talk about the prophylaxis of venereal disease – having been reminded, presumably, by seeing the report in my hand.

'A fascinating subject, that. Of course all the moralists from Old Testament times onward have warned people that the only sure way of preventing what we now call venereal diseases is by continence. And of course they're right. But only a minority of people have ever put the advice into practice. The great ages of promiscuity – the sixteenth and seventeenth centuries and the century we're living in now, for example – show the greatest epidemics of venereal diseases. And because people have always wanted to eat their cake and keep it too there have been plenty of efforts to find means to prevent infection during sexual intercourse. The most effective of these is the contraceptive sheath, but, unless the records have failed to survive, it isn't by any means the earliest. Fallopius, the sixteenth-century Italian anatomist, described a prophylactic method which involved the wearing of a wrapping of silk impregnated with mercury and other substances over the penis during intercourse; and eighteenth-century medical literature abounds with details of supposedly prophylactic ointments and liquids that were to be used for cleansing the genitalia. Mercury, alcohol, and caustic potash form the basis of most of them, and they probably often had some effect. But Fallopius's silk wrapping, if effective at all, would have been so only because of the mercury used to impregnate it – and then only in cases of syphilis, for mercury, as you know, has no effect on gonorrhoea. It wouldn't actually have prevented the venereal germs being transmitted from one partner to the other. You need something non-porous for that, and the male rubber contraceptive sheath is the nearest you'll get to success. So far, anyway.

'There doesn't seem to be any reason why a contraceptive

sheath is called in common parlance a French Letter. "French" quite likely because of the association with French pox; but why "letter"? I don't know. You might like to try your etymologist friend Mr Partridge again. But there's a supposed reason why it's also called a condom: a Doctor Condom is credited with inventing it in the early eighteenth century. Another theory is that "condom" is a corruption or adaptation of the Latin "*condere*", which means to protect; and if that theory's right it implies that the sheath was in use in Roman times. I've never come across any other evidence that it was, though. But there were certainly sheaths in use in the eighteenth century. They were made of the caeca of sheep – that's a sort of pouch the intestine fits into – and if you'll hand me down Dunglinson's *Dictionary of Medical Science* from that shelf there I'll tell you how they were made.'

I handed him the book and when he'd found the page he continued: 'There you are: "The intestinal caecum of a sheep, soaked for some hours in water, turned inside out, macerated again in weak alkaline changed every twelve hours, scraped carefully to abstract the mucous membrane, leaving the peritoneal and muscular coats exposed to the vapour of burning brimstone, and afterwards washed with soap and water. It is then blown up, dried, cut to the length of seven or eight inches, and bordered at the open end with a riband. It is drawn over the penis prior to coition, to prevent venereal infection and pregnancy." I see that I've added a note I've copied from some other book. It says: "These machines were long prepared and sold by a matron of the name of Phillips, at the sign of the Green Canister in Half-Moon Street. That good lady having acquired a fortune, retired from business; but learning that the town was not well served by her successors, she, out of patriotic welfare, returned to her occupation; of which she gave notice by divers handbills, in circulation in the year 1776." I dare say Mrs Phillips made a fortune by charging excessive prices for her sheaths, but I don't doubt she was a public benefactress. There isn't anything better as a preventive against infection.'

He paused, swung round in his chair to put the book on the table, then continued with an added note of severity: 'But don't go saying it's an *unfailing* preventive. It isn't – any more than it's an unfailing method of preventing insemination. As you see from that report you've been reading there's quite a high percentage of faulty sheaths turned out. And in any case it's easily possible to be infected by other parts of the body than the genitalia. The mouth, for instance. You remember me telling you that a number of my patients were doctors and dentists who'd got V.D. in the course of duty? Well, the dentists picked it up by examining the mouths of syphilitics. And the trunk and limbs can be acutely infectious in the early stages of syphilis. So can clothing and towels that have been impregnated with gonorrhoeal discharges. But apart from abstention from any kind of sexual intercourse with unknown partners the sheath is the best method of prophylaxis. Washing with soap and water and the use of various ointments are helpful too, and in wartime, when soldiers are exposed to the risk of infection, army medical authorities issue free sheaths and what they call Early Treatment packets, plus dire warnings about the dangers of promiscuous intercourse. I don't think the warnings ever make much difference, though. Soldiers, like a good many civilians, don't find it convenient to use sheaths or go through the rather finicky business of disinfection. The ideal thing, of course, would be some kind of vaccine that people could be inoculated with, as they're inoculated against smallpox. But we haven't invented one yet. And if one came to be invented it would naturally pose the moral problem of seeming to encourage promiscuity. So there you are. Although we all know that prevention's better than cure, it's cure that occupies most doctors' time.'

This seemed a natural cue for my questions about treatment, and I asked him to explain to me, first, the kind of approach usually made by new patients, secondly the routine of examination, and thirdly how he decided what treatment to give.

'Right,' he said. 'One: the patient's approach. Naturally this varies with the individual, but they tend to fall into a pattern.

Usually they say, either boldly or apologetically, according to their character, that they suspect they've "picked something up". I ask them why they think that. They explain that they've been with somebody while drunk, or that they've recently heard that their sexual partner is infected, or they've seen actual signs on their own body – discharge, rash, sore, swelling, whatever it may be. The next step is to ask more questions. When was the infection supposedly acquired? – I need to know that because of the incubation period – what sort of signs have they seen? Any pains? Any previous venereal infections? No question that might give the slightest clue must be left unasked. Then the examination. The majority of venereal cases are of course gonorrhoea – that being, as I said before, the world's most prevalent disease bar one: measles. Gonorrhoea is comparatively easy to identify. There may be a scalding sensation during urination, accompanied by a discharge. You take a sample of this discharge on a loop of platinum wire, spread it on a clean glass slide and fix it there by passing it through a flame, stain the slide so that the germs will show up, and put it under the microscope. Then you can identify the gonococci – if they're there of course. They usually are – though occasionally there's some confusion between gonorrhoea and a non-venereal, but sexual, disease that's popularly known as "husband's clap", which has somewhat similar symptoms and is caused by having intercourse when one of the partners is below par in health or when the woman's period is imminent. You can do this test for gonococci while the patient's waiting, so you don't have to keep him – or her – in suspense. The treatment is invariably penicillin or one of the sulpha drugs, or both, in whatever happens to be the best form for that particular case. It'll depend largely on whether it's a mild or severe, acute, sub-acute, or chronic case. And the length and success of the treatment will naturally depend on that too.

'Syphilis isn't nearly so easy to identify. My expert eye may immediately identify a syphilitic chancre or swelling, but that isn't nearly enough for confirmation. We use a test called the Wassermann reaction, which was the discovery of a German bacteriologist of that name. You take a sample of the patient's blood from a vein in the crook of the elbow and put it in a sterile test tube, where you let it clot. In clotting, the blood becomes separated from the serum and you keep the serum and throw the clot away. Then you destroy the complement in the serum by heating it – you look puzzled. Am I going too fast?'

'Not too fast,' I said. 'I don't quite understand "complement" in this context.'

'Ah. Complement is the substance in serum that combines with antibodies to destroy bacteria. You mix the serum with an extract of beef heart fortified with alcohol, and add this mixture to another mixture of sheep's blood and rabbit's serum. The reaction you get will indicate whether the patient's serum is syphilitic. But that still isn't nearly enough to go on – and in fact it isn't any use at all in the earliest stage of the disease. You remember I wrote in that little book how important it is to be absolutely certain before you tell your patient he's got syphilis? This isn't just because of the legal angle: a patient worrying about syphilis is under great mental strain and must have his suspicions confirmed or denied with accuracy. Also, as you know there are a great many things that can be confused with syphilis. So a Wassermann test isn't enough in itself. You make an elaborate examination of the patient from top to toe – every inch of skin, the scalp, the mucous membranes, the bones, the glands, the liver, the spleen; and you take scrapings from any sores there may be and put them under the microscope to see if *Spirochaeta* are present. In fact you leave no possible opening for a false diagnosis. All these tests will take some time: except for the examination and the microscope test you can't do them while the patient is waiting; so you try to relieve him of some of his worry by assuring him of the efficacy of treatment these days. And it is, for the most part, very successful. Nearly everything depends on how early you begin treatment. Don't forget that syphilitic lesions often disappear completely if left entirely un-treated, and the disease pursues its course silently and invisibly. The patient may be in the tertiary stage, with the syphilitic destruction of some organ well advanced, before he comes to you. And you can't rebuild that destroyed tissue – only prevent further destruction.

'As for the treatment I decide on – well, I only have to remind you: "every case is different". Penicillin most probably; but there are people who are allergic to it; and in any case it sometimes isn't enough on its own. I might reinforce its effect with bismuth, with one of the arsenobenzenes, or even with mercury or one of the iodides. How would I decide? is what you want to ask now. And I can't give you an answer that would apply to every case. In a lifetime's experience you acquire a good deal of know-how that you can't put into words. That know-how often tells you what treatment a particular case will best react to. But quite often, too, you change the treatment according to the reaction of the disease. The patient may have to continue coming to you for many months, perhaps years, for continual examination. And it's an unpredictable disease, as I've told you. You may get negative Wassermann reactions and the apparent destruction of every *Spirochaeta* in the body and have this seeming cure followed by a relapse. That might mean completely different treatment. One way and another I can't be more specific than that. I assure you, though, that I haven't abandoned or forgotten any of the treatments you've worked so studiously to explain to your readers. Some doctors pooh-pooh the effectiveness of some of the older ones as compared with penicillin and even newer drugs; but it's safest not to pooh-pooh anything in medicine. It's also safest for the patient to come for regular examinations after he's apparently cured, so that I can watch for signs of any relapse. Now, have you got all that? If so, I dare say you'll be glad of a respite from my clinical chattering.'

I had in fact been absorbed by it. But it was getting late, a clammy fog was settling down on the streets, and I took my leave. I had an uneasy feeling that my forty-mile journey home might be difficult, and my apprehension was justified. At the station there was a milling throng of people and a fog service in operation. I decided to stay the night in town at my club, and, knowing that the Doctor's home was nearby I rang him up and asked him if he'd join me for dinner.

'I'd be delighted,' he said. 'But you'll understand if I get called away half-way through the fish. It's an occupational hazard of doctors. If I don't, we can go on talking happily through this ghostly evening.'

I imagined I'd misheard and that he meant 'ghastly'. But I hadn't misheard at all.

# 9 *A Battle for the Sword*

'It occurred to me,' the Doctor said, 'that we might get away from the consulting-room in both senses of the word. Seeing this fog come down tonight evoked a lot of misty memories. I don't mean of incidents on similar foggy evenings years ago, or of ghosts – though I shall have one of those to tell you about another time – but of what I suppose you might call an interlude in my medical career. I mean the war. Not that it was an interlude in the strict sense – I was a doctor in it, naturally – but I was away from St Martin's. The spell of medicine, in the sense of being able to do research and work on individual patients, was broken – just as the spell of the consulting-room has been broken for us by this foggy night and your kind invitation. You see the parallel?'

I saw the parallel and thought it was a good parallel and said so; and the Doctor told me that he had tried to clarify his misty memories during his unpleasant walk to the club. As we stood with our backs to the fire drinking aperitifs he had the slightly amused look of a man who unexpectedly sees himself as the old-fashioned club yarn spinner holding forth. As if enjoying this thought he stepped into character at once, one hand behind him under his jacket, the other holding his copita of Amontillado as he swayed slightly on heel and toe.

'The walk here didn't exactly offer an encouraging atmosphere for dispelling mists,' he said, 'but I think I managed to get things sorted out more or less chronologically.'

He told me how in the spring of 1916 he decided to join the navy and how the navy's representative rudely rejected him when he offered his services as a doctor. 'We don't want any people like you in the navy' were the words used to him in the recruiting office in the Admiralty. Not surprisingly, the Doctor wasn't pleased by this charmless response and straightaway walked across the road from the Admiralty to the War Office, where he was immediately made a lieutenant in the Royal Army Medical Corps, and told that his commission was honorary and unpaid until he was called to report for service. A short time later his call came and he presented himself for training at Codford Camp on Salisbury Plain, where he went through the usual routine of physical training and bareback riding on irascible horses (the R.A.M.C. was, rather oddly, a cavalry regiment), plus parade-ground drill under an irascible Sergeant-Major. He remembered little about this training period – it lasted only three weeks – except that it left him with the insides of his legs blistered from riding bareback, and that the doctor who inoculated the trainees against typhoid used a single rusty needle in a dirty syringe to jab forty men. (This last was a slight shock, since before he left St Martin's the Doctor had spent many months doing surgery under complete asepsis; and he had the nerve to protest to the Australian major who was doing the jabbing – without much effect, for the major only snarled in the conventional army manner, 'You're in the army now; *you* don't think, *I* do the thinking.')

On 12th June, 1916, he was told by the Adjutant that he'd been selected to proceed on draft to India, and, mildly surprised he remarked, 'That's a long way, and there's no fighting there, is there?' Whether or not this questioning comment had any influence on the subsequent change of plan cannot be proved. The Doctor thinks it did. At all events, he embarked a week later not for India but for France. There he was temporarily attached to a large hospital at Etretat, a few miles north of Le Havre, and from there, at the end of June, was ordered to the front to join the 34th Division. The train was packed with reinforcements for every branch of the service, but no one had the smallest idea where the front was or where the train was going. It moved mysteriously day and night, making wide detours and confusing reverse movements so that after a while it became impossible to tell whether they had been separated from Etretat by five miles or five hundred. All leave had been stopped, all officers had been recalled to duty, and it was forbidden to post letters. The countryside was deserted and, up to the time night fell and for several hours the following morning, there was no sign of war. But at last the train reached a rail-head at Mericourt and while it was shunted into a siding the Doctor bought a cup of tea, a piece of cake, a packet of De Reszke cigarettes, and a spare collar-stud from a local canteen. He had a notion that this might be the last outpost of civilization he'd see for some time.

A few days later, on the 1st July, the battle of the Somme began. The Doctor was attached to the 102nd Field Ambulance of the 102nd Brigade, which was in the 34th Division (commanded by Major-General E. C. Ingouville-Williams, CB, DSO, and later by Major-General Sir Lothian Nicholson, KCB, CMG), and his headquarters was at Franvillers, near the main road from Amiens to Albert.

'The country round Albert was rolling downs, a few trees, no hedges. There were villages in ruins and an occasional chateau visible through clumps of trees. Albert itself – a small town – was empty and in ruins. The aid-post of our Field Ambulance was in the cellars – full of rats, they were – of the École Supérieur in the square in the middle of the town, under the shadow of the basilica. I remember that on top of the belfry was a statue of the Virgin Mary holding up the Child. The statue had been turned by our engineers so that it was at right angles to the belfry and parallel with the ground so that the enemy couldn't use it as a range-finding mark, and in this curious position it seemed to be blessing the square and the ruined town. Albert had been evacuated six days previously in expectation of a German bombardment, which duly arrived, a single shell killing eight out of ten medical officers who were eating a meal in the cellar. I'd been sent forward to replace one of these, and believe me I had plenty to do. You'll find if you read any objective report on the battle of the Somme that it was one of the bloodiest and worst planned battles in history. We had more troops, more artillery, and more machine-guns per mile than the

Germans; but we simply didn't know how to plan and co-ordi-
nate. The battle was on such a colossal scale that the top people
couldn't – and certainly didn't – understand the planning that
was essential for such a venture. Haig, who was in charge,
thought we had an undefeatable force. And no doubt the
courage of individual troops was magnificent. But courage won't
get you far when a high proportion of the shells you're firing are
duds and either go off prematurely as they leave the gun barrel
– killing the unfortunate team that fires – or don't go off at all.
Nor will such farcical moves as sending the cavalry up to the
trenches daily to "charge through the gap" – which is what the
orders were. There wasn't any gap to charge through. But sure
enough every morning up came these unfortunate cavalrymen
with lances at the ready and pennons flying – marvellously spec-
tacular! but getting in the way of motorized transport bringing
guns and supplies we desperately needed – and back they went
in the evening as "retreat" was sounded, in the gentlemanly way
of battles of centuries ago, when fighting stopped at sundown
and everybody collected up their dead from the battlefield and
went home to bed for the night. And can you imagine so little
attention being paid to security? As I told you, the journey from
the coast to the rail-head at Mericourt was shrouded in mystery;
but as soon as we got to the front line we were told by all and
sundry in general conversation the times and dates of all our
moves, so I don't doubt for a moment that what I heard – that
the date and time of our initial bombardment, which began on
the twenty-fifth of June, was known weeks in advance – was
true. There were spies everywhere – civilians wandering about –
and no one took the slightest notice of them. Can you wonder
that the Germans were fully prepared? Can you wonder that
our losses were so great? By the end of that first day of
battle on July the first we had lost sixty thousand men; and by
the end of the month we had lost a hundred and seventy-one
thousand and had advanced less than three miles over ground
that wasn't of the slightest strategic value. It was mad. Mad!'

The Doctor's memory of the shambles of the Somme battle

had caught him up in an emotional involvement that expressed itself in a way unfamiliar to me. His evident anger had cancelled out his impersonation of one of the club's elder statesmen and he was simply himself – a man enraged at the waste of life due to lack of foresight. This lack of foresight, he told me as we went in to dinner, was nowhere more apparent than in the skimpy equipment he was issued with.

'I had a pannier which contained bandages, some lint, a bottle of sal volatile, some iodine, and a bottle of quarter-grain morphia tablets. Nothing else whatever. No instruments of any kind, nothing even that could be used as a splint. A man with a broken limb had to have it splinted with his rifle or bayonet; and a man with his belly ripped open and his guts tumbling out simply got the guts pushed back in and a morphia tablet pushed under his tongue. I remember coming on one chap – a German – hanging on a dannert fence – coiled barbed wire, you know – with his body ripped open from the navel to the chin by a shell splinter. Amazingly, he was still alive but obviously impossible to repair. I gave him a handful of morphia tablets to finish him off– probably about twenty tablets, enough to finish off a dozen men. But two days later he was still alive, his guts flapping on the wire in the pouring rain. Amazing the endurance of the human body. Now what do you advise from this excellent menu? A grilled sole, perhaps?'

The bombardment that had begun on the 25th of June continued unceasingly for weeks. Night and day the swish of shells and the booming of the guns filled the air. Two hours after the slaughter of the Somme officially began at 7.30 a.m. on the 1st of July the Doctor was dressing casualties more quickly than he thought possible; by the evening of the next day the pitiful remnants of the 34th Division were officially taken out of the front line. (Not that this made much difference in practice. The division was not in fact evacuated until 11 a.m. on the following Tuesday morning.) The last casualties the Doctor had to attend to at his advanced aid post were twenty Scots maddened by shellfire.

'They'd been buried in their trench and dug out and they manifested the usual symptoms of intense shock. But five of them were in a different category; they'd obviously suffered much greater damage to their nervous systems – perhaps because they'd been buried more deeply than the rest. This had reacted on them in an odd fashion. They had no wounds or broken limbs, but they wandered about aimlessly, terrified, with no volition of their own. And their hair was standing on end. Every hair on their scalps stood erect, not momentarily but continuously. It was so stiffly erect that it held their caps right off their heads, you couldn't even thrust the caps down by using force. And when, after a while a few hairs began to lose their rigidity at the ends and curl limply downward, they were immediately erected again whenever the swish of a shell was heard. Naturally I was interested in these rather special cases, but I didn't have the opportunity to observe them as closely as I'd have liked. I did, however, separate them from the others – they were upsetting morale a bit – and herded them into a sort of stockade near the bank of sandbags where the stretcher-bearers were dumping the wounded as fast – faster – than I could deal with them. This stockade was no more than a rectangle of posts joined with wire. It had an entrance without a gate and had probably been used to keep a few farm animals together. I posted a sentry at the entrance and got on with my work until I could do something about getting them evacuated. But from time to time as I straightened up from binding a wound – dirt and all, for there was no water to wash anything with – I saw them grovelling on the floor of the stockade, clawing at the earth with their fingers and biting at it with their teeth – presumably they were going through the motions of digging shelters for themselves. Then one of them went berserk. He was a sergeant-major – a fine, big strong chap. One minute he was grovelling on the floor and the next he must have glimpsed a half-dozen German prisoners being brought in, for he had knocked the sentry aside and dashed through the entrance and across the few yards to where the prisoners were being guarded by their escort. He seized two of the prisoners round their necks, throttled them, and bashed their two skulls together. His momentary colossal strength smashed their heads completely – they might have been in giant nutcrackers. They couldn't have been deader. Then all the sergeant-major's strength vanished. He just burst into tears and we led him away and evacuated him to a rear casualty clearing station with a luggage label hanging from his tunic. I don't know whether he – or any of them – ever recovered.'

The Doctor's sole arrived and the waiter asked him if he would like it taken off the bone. 'Why, no,' he said. 'I shall enjoy dissecting it.' Which he obviously did. And while he was operating on the fish he continued his story of the Somme.

'When that Scottish sergeant-major killed the two prisoners he was of course experiencing the condition we refer to idiomatically as "seeing red". I experienced this sensation myself once during the war – and only once. I was crouching down in a battered trench – it had been so battered that it didn't deserve the name of trench any more – when a five-point-nine shell came down and hit one of our chaps. The four stretcher-bearers beside me immediately went over to bring him in so that I could give him some kind of attention. And as they were laying him on the stretcher another shell made a direct hit on them. All five were blown to bits and the pieces scattered about. I know perfectly well that if a German had been within reach – I'd have torn him apart with my bare hands. I could feel the extra strength *there*. The fact that there was no one about on whom I could wreak my vengeance made me feel dreadfully impotent but didn't decrease my rage in the least. That was really the only time I felt anything approaching murderous anger – the only time in my life, I think I can say with honesty. Ordinary everyday anger, such as one feels as a consequence of the stupidity of other people – that's a different thing. I felt that many times on the Somme and have felt it many times since. But even that alternated with a kind of desperate pride when I saw the ardour with which our chaps flung themselves into battle. Strange how that kind of ardour is infectious. I remember that at the time I felt glad I was in this biggest of battles. Can you imagine? *Glad!* It was exciting, fast, everything going on all the time all round you. The knowledge that our chaps had captured an objective; then the anguish when they'd lost it again; and the horror as you realized in brief flashes the extent of our losses. They were all fragmentary impressions, you see, extremes of emotion veering first one way and then another. And occasionally – only very occasionally – one was aware of one's body, its filth, its need of nourishment and sleep. I went without sleep for eight days and scarcely noticed the lack because it was a long nightmare of patching up thousands of bloody wounds and shattered bones with virtually nothing to patch them up with. But if I'd been on sentry duty I probably wouldn't have been able to overcome my body's demand for sleep. Many sentries didn't. They fell asleep on the firing-steps of their trenches and if they were discovered they were said to be endangering the lives of their comrades – which they were of course – and they were given summary courts-martial in due course and shot. As if it wasn't enough to have the enemy killing us in thousands! – as we were to a smaller extent killing them too. In retrospect, sitting here finishing this very good sole, you see the mad irony of it. But at the time . . . no. I remember thinking – writing, even, in very scrappy notes when eventually we were taken out of the front line – that I wouldn't have missed it for worlds.'

The Doctor smiled at the oddity of human responses, put on his glasses to read the menu, and asked for a savoury to follow his sole.

'Eventually,' he continued, 'what was left of the division was taken a few miles back to Mericourt to rest. There were only three thousand left of the eighteen thousand that went into battle. We had a week's respite and then returned to Albert and were promoted to being a Corps ambulance unit instead of a Divisional one. Down in the cellars, where we slept, ate, and worked on the wounded, the rats seemed to have multiplied. They crept all over me as I grabbed brief half-hours of sleep on

the earth floor. And when I lit my cigarette lighter the flame
made their eyes gleam – hundreds of little yellow pinpoints of
light. I didn't care for the rats, and when I managed to get hold
of a candle I kept it burning beside me. It helped to keep them
off a bit. But then an eight-inch "Jack Johnson" shell would
land somewhere outside and blow out the candle and a few
more lives; so the rats paled into insignificance. But a few days
later we were moved back a couple of miles to the Amiens road,
and lived in tents which were infested with spiders and beetles
which I tried to keep down by soaking the floors with creosote.
By that time I had more than enough of war and was sick of
being unable to use my medical and surgical skill for lack of
equipment – any orderly could have done what I did. It had
become a monotonous succession of blown-off limbs and ripped-
out guts. I'd had enough excitement to last me for the rest of my
life. But it was only about the second week in August then, and,
as I expect you know, the battle of the Somme went on till
November. I didn't, though.'

The Doctor paused and drank some wine, then set down the
glass and turned it gently round and round on the table as he
reassembled his memories. All traces of his anger had vanished
now. As I could tell from the slight smile that parted his lips to
show a gold tooth-filling, he was amused by some reminiscence
that had just occurred to him.

'I was working hard one day, going from casualty to casualty
– they lay strewn around on the ground – and came to a chap
who'd had half an arm blown off. It was very hot and I'd taken
my tunic off and was applying a tourniquet – it was just a
bandage tightened with a bayonet – when a bit of top brass came
up to me. He was the Deputy Assistant Director of Medical
Services, a chap who'd joined the regular army as a doctor two
days after he'd qualified – not a scrap of hospital or any other
kind of experience. He said, "You're improperly dressed – your
spur chain is twisted, and your shirt is hanging out." He was
right: during the previous night my ammunition boots and
puttees had been soaking wet and I'd changed them for my

riding boots, which I'd put on in the dark. Then I'd gone out to
bring in a wounded man who'd got entangled in some barbed
wire and the struggle to get him off had ripped my Bedford cord
breeches, so naturally my shirt was hanging out. Also, I was
dirty and unshaven; but I snapped back at the D.A.D.M.S. that
getting the wounded attended to was more important than army
tripe. A bit later I was transferred to another regiment as a
supposed punishment. This was the Thirteenth Royal Fusiliers,
but it didn't make much difference which regiment you were
attached to – there were plenty of casualties with all of them. I
suppose it might have made a bit of difference to my army
service, though, because while I was with the Thirteenth I got
something wrong with my chest. I'd been regimental gas officer
for some time, which meant that I had to test our own gas shells
and gas masks – they were elementary things like Ku Klux
Klan hoods, made of flannel – by actually inhaling the gases for
identification purposes; and I'd been about when German gas
shells had come over. So I'd picked up poisoning by phosgene
and it had affected my lungs. I was examined by three doctors
of One-o-Four Field Ambulance and they decided I'd have to go
back to the Casualty Clearing Station at Bailleul. There I was
examined again and sent even farther back to the hospital at
Calais. (All this took several days, naturally, and all the time I
was on a milk diet – I've just remembered it because I'm enjoying this grilled roe so much.) Then at Calais it was decided
they could do nothing more for me and I was put aboard an
ambulance train and shipped back to London. I'd been right
when I'd bought that packet of cigarettes and collar stud and
thought I might not see civilization again for some time. I found
myself on a stretcher at Charing Cross Station and everybody
who was milling round was anxious to do something for me. I
was dirty and unshaved and muddy and my uniform was in
rags, but I was asked where I wanted to go to and I said immediately "St Martin's", so that a bit later I arrived at the casualty
entrance where I'd so often been on duty myself and was given
the real V.I.P. treatment – with a bed in one of the "paying"

wards instead of a free public one. I was given a thorough
examination and found to be suffering from a left-sided pleural
effusion and D.A.H. – disordered action of the heart – and it
was confirmed that these were due to poisoning from phosgene
gas. Exactly six months after I'd gone into action on the Somme
– that is, on the first of December, nineteen-sixteen, I appeared
before a medical board at the War Office, where a doctor
examined me with an old-fashioned wooden stethoscope and
said I'd be discharged from the army. I was astonished at this
and asked why. The doctor seemed equally astonished at my
astonishment and asked me, Didn't I want to get out of the
army? I said no, not while there was a war on, and he went into
a huddle with some other officers and they decided to give me
sick leave followed by light duties at Dover garrison. But I wasn't
wanted there because the place was already crowded with sick
medical officers who couldn't be given any light duties because
there weren't any light duties to give them; and in the end the
examining doctors' first decision was reverted to and I was forced
to take my discharge from the army, which I finally did
in February, nineteen-seventeen. I went back to St Martin's and
they were only too pleased to give me an appointment at once.
I'd been away just under a year.'

We had our coffee and then, since it seemed appropriate to
the occasion, I took the Doctor up to the library and we looked
out of the window where Sir Edward Grey is traditionally supposed to have stood on the eve of war in 1914, watching the
Embankment lamps being extinguished and being prompted to
his observation that the lamps were going out all over Europe.
They were not out now, but the fog had diminished them to
nebulous penumbrae. There was no sound at all from the
scarcely visible, barely moving lines of traffic, but the Doctor
said, quite unaffectedly, that, listening hard, he could still hear
the ghostly battalions marching to the Somme.

# 10 *Experiment and Achievement*

While the Doctor had been in France an Act of Parliament had authorized the establishment of a Venereal Diseases Department at St Martin's. The dire need for this was of course one of the consequences of war, but the need had hardly been less dire previously. Moral obloquy, however, had not become less important than epidemic infection and go-ahead signals were being made tardily but frantically in every direction. One thing the alarm led to was the publication, by the British Social Hygiene Council, of a pamphlet entitled *How To Fight Venereal Disease*. This showed on the cover a female figure of stern aspect dressed in a flowing robe labelled 'commonsense' and a peculiar hat labelled 'hygiene'. This symbolic figure held aloft a torch and with the other hand pierced, with a sword marked 'knowledge', a very dead dragon labelled 'venereal disease' In the background were symbolic representations of 'waste', 'insanity', 'mortality', and 'decay'. Inside the pamphlet were charts and statistics showing how ante-natal treatment of syphilitic mothers resulted in more than twice the number of healthy children being born.

The Doctor was not especially interested in venereology. His particular leaning was toward surgery and he intended to take the higher degree (M.S.) in this subject after the war. He was of course already a Member of the Royal College of Surgeons and a Licentiate of the Royal College of Physicians, these having been the qualifying degrees he earned earlier, but specialization demands advanced study in the chosen field and higher degrees are a corollary of this. However, circumstances eventuated to redirect his plans. The hospital Governors had appointed a doctor whom I will call Falkner to found and take charge of the new department and the appointment the Doctor was given after being discharged from the army was that of his assistant. He pursued his plan to turn his career to that of surgeon to the extent of resigning eventually to work for his Fellowship (as distinct from Membership) of the Royal College of Surgeons and his Mastership of Surgery; but within a couple of months Mr Falkner fell ill with tuberculosis and the Doctor was summoned to take charge of the Department. He could of course have refused, but to have done so would have meant killing the career he aimed for as a surgeon in his own teaching hospital, etiquette being extremely strict in the matter of accepting and refusing appointments. He therefore abandoned his plan with good grace and, having satisfied himself with the additional degrees of Bachelor of Medicine and Bachelor of Surgery took charge of the Venereal Department.

Having started to specialize in venereology by force of circumstances he soon became intensely interested in it and began to write medical papers on various aspects of the subject. One of these offered a method of determining or prognosticating whether or not a patient was afflicted with the earliest stages of tabes or general paresis, and if so, which. In plainer words, if a patient was heading for general paralysis of the insane, or for tabes, the chronic syphilitic wasting that leads to death, the fact could be determined in time for anticipatory treatment to be given.

Clearly, his research as revealed by publication of this paper was of the utmost importance. The study of medicine is continually concerned with anticipating the activities of the enmitous organisms – bacilli and viruses – that doctors and research chemists are for ever fighting. Like generals in an army they need continual and effective intelligence of the enemy's movements and designs. A general, however, has one great advantage on his side in his battles. However inhuman, in a moral sense, the enemy may be, the workings of his mind are inevitably human. His designs may be wickedly cunning or extremely simple; but whatever they are they will be the designs of a brain that is organically the same as the brain of whoever is planning for 'our' side – who is, of course, the 'enemy's' enemy. And in the light of the recorded experiences of earlier generals in history 'our' general can assess the probabilities of his enemy's future plans. If he is able to add to his own perception practical knowledge of the details of those plans he is in a much stronger position to defeat them. And such knowledge is gained only by an efficient intelligence service, which in turn depends on the outwitting of one human brain by another – a situation we are all familiar with in spy stories in which spies and counter-spies doublecross each other until the reader is practically crosseyed.

But the scientist in his battles against bacilli and viruses can-not equate his brain with another of similar calibre. These creatures haven't acquired brains : they have only instincts to guide them in their evolution towards what one supposes is, in the germ world, better living. And instincts are not fully under-stood in the human world, let alone any other. (No-one, for example, has yet satisfactorily explained the migratory instinct of certain birds.) The battle is one of blows delivered, as it were, into some soft plastic substance which disappears from the point of impact only to splurge out elsewhere. Responding to instinct, the enemy displays what might be thought of in human terms as low cunning; but, as I say, one cannot think in human terms. And the battle progresses on an extremely chancy hit-or-miss basis. Ehrlich and countless other scientists make their hundreds and thousands of experiments because they are necessary, not because they have nothing else to do. They hope that each one will bring destruction of the enemy nearer, or, if nothing else, that they will discover what in a human battle would be called information about the enemy's movements.

This was exactly what the Doctor did – in an immensely long and complex series of experiments. To be able to determine whether a patient was heading for tabes or general paresis (with-out necessarily being able to cure him) may sound no more important than being able to tell him that he had either a common cold or influenza; but in the world of venereology it was an achievement of alpha-double-plus importance; and in the broader medical world where specialists inhabit their own small domains and the general practitioner keeps an eye on everything it was thought of with almost equal awe. The profession of medicine is austere, but the success of experiments does not pass unnoticed. Flutterings in the doctors' dovecotes may not generate excitement comparable with that attending a newly successful pop singing group, but they are not inaudible.

The Doctor's interest in venereology was sharpened considerably by the epidemic proportions the diseases had attained during the war years. 'If anything was needed to convince me that venereologists were needed more desperately than surgeons,' he said, 'it was the astonishing number of patients who came to the St Martin's clinic for treatment.' He rose and went to one of the drawers in an untidily stuffed filing cabinet and without hesitation put his hand on a couple of graphs which he brought over for me to see. 'There : in nineteen-seventeen, as you see, the number of new venereal cases in men from London and the home counties alone was slightly over eight thousand; by nineteen-twenty it had risen to eighteen thousand. But those were just new cases. In nineteen-nineteen two hundred thousand men were attending clinics for treatment; a year later this figure had risen to three hundred and twenty-five thousand; and by nineteen-thirty to over six hundred thousand. No doubt the actual number of infected people was ten times as large. One of my greatest difficulties was to encourage more and more people to attend, and this was always much harder with women than with men. There are a number of reasons why people are reluctant to attend V.D. clinics – some of them psychological and some medical – and all of them are more important to women than to men.

'Ignorance is of course at the bottom of the chief psychological reason. For generations venereal diseases have been tabooed in this country. Two results of this ignorance are the exaggeration of natural feminine modesty into excessive timidity toward doctors and hospitals, and the indifference of many women toward consequences which, if thought about, might make having what they call "a good time" ever again quite hopeless. Then there's the moral guilt that's so closely associated with the public taboo I mentioned just now. The majority of women feel ashamed and deceive themselves into thinking they've got a chill or some such euphemistic nonsense. They also dread to think that they've been deceived by their partners, in whom they often have a touching faith. Then they're alarmed by notices in public lavatories and work themselves up into an anxiety neurosis which prevents them going to have their suspicions confirmed. Instead they go to dubious chemists and back-street quacks and rely on useless ointments, douches, and tonics. They also cling quite unwarrantably to the idea that V.D. is caused by dirt. And one of the most powerful psychological deterrents to attendance is the fear of meeting people they know, being recognized going into or coming out of the clinic.

'Then there are medical reasons. Regrettably, one of the most important of these in the early days of V.D. clinics was the inefficiency of the staff – and I don't exempt the doctors, who, God knows, had the opportunity to specialize but often didn't bother. Women often believe, too, that non-menstrual vaginal discharges are part of God's burden for women or some such nonsense, and that douching with lysol is an infallible remedy. Equally, as I've said before, they think that contraceptive measures are an infallible preventive of both conception and infection. Mill girls in the north of England grab a handful of tow, roll it into a tampon which they thrust into the vaginal passage, and go off with their boy-friends ready for anything. I need hardly say that they haven't all that cause for optimism. Another medical reason for the difficulty of getting women to attend for treatment is that the symptoms of gonorrhœa are not so painful for them as for men and the disease often reaches the stage of complications before they venture to seek advice. Then they probably start off with some busy general practitioner who perhaps isn't able to spend a lot of time on a pelvic examination and just prescribes some astringent douche which dries up the discharge but doesn't cure the infection. One way and another, you see, there were plenty of reasons why the diseases were gaining a grip of epidemic proportions in spite of vastly increased attendances at clinics for treatment: the numbers affected were always 'way ahead of the numbers who sought advice – especially among women.'

Having given me this rapid exposition of some of the problems that faced him during his term of office at the St Martin's clinic, the Doctor scarcely paused for breath before he was off again on an outline of the combative measures he planned. As he pointed out, the venereologists who preceded him – from Fracastorious onward – would have wasted their energies in the forging of the therapeutic sword, and he himself would have wasted his energies on the Somme battling for the freedom to swing it in, if he hadn't tried to sharpen its edge still more and tried also to get people into its field of power.

'The first combative action, of course, was simply the acquisition of knowledge by way of research. But the other was a more mundane but equally important activity: dealing with people. I gradually got the staff – the porter at the door and every member of the department through every phase of reception, examination, and treatment – to try and counteract the effects of timidity and ignorance. I pointed out that the reception of a patient must be courteous, that the name and address must be obtained quietly so as not to be overheard, and that he should be examined as soon as possible. I so often found that apprehension increased in people who were kept waiting, so that they changed their minds and walked out. Also, I insisted that patients should never be treated as if they were criminals – a discourtesy that had happened all too often. I have actually heard women being asked point-blank if they were prostitutes, and I can't imagine anything less likely to encourage attendance at a clinic. All my staff had to learn the art of questioning and to use some sense of psychology in differentiating between all kinds of people. A young, timid, terrified girl is made even more

embarrassed by being asked intimate questions, while a professional street girl may be quite unconcerned. But it's often quite
unnecessary to ask such intimate questions : the thing to do is to
gain the confidence of the patient, who will then invariably
answer the questions before you ask them. And another thing
that must be avoided is giving the impression of being in a hurry
– very difficult, because so often you are. But it's only by taking
the time to explain, in simple words but without causing increased alarm, the dangers of neglect, that you can convince the
patient. The greatest advantage of all, of course, is to have
*specializing* doctors and ample money to be used solely for the
fighting of V.D. In practice one never has enough of either.
Venereology doesn't attract doctors – probably, I think, because
it may seem too narrow a field of specialization. Doctors, like
many other people, like variety; and suppose there's more variety
in, say, general surgery, pædiatrics, gynæcology, heart diseases,
industrial diseases, cancer, diseases of the nervous system, ob-
stetrics, orthopaedics – I could name another dozen specialities.
Nurses are also a big difficulty. In most teaching hospitals the
nurses' duties are changed every few months so that they get the
necessary general experience. But people with V.D. dread seeing
new faces every time they go for treatment, so, ideally, the same
nurse and the same doctor should see them at every visit. As for
the money side – well, it's essential that those who can't afford
to pay for treatment should have it just the same and of course
nowadays they do – but only because a Royal Commission on
Venereal Diseases sat from nineteen-thirteen to nineteen-sixteen
and caused the Venereal Diseases Act to be passed in nineteen-
seventeen and many clinics were established as a result. These
public clinics have met a most urgent need and the fact that
venereal diseases are to some extent – note that I emphasise that
"some" – under control nowadays is very largely due to that
Venereal Diseases Act of nineteen-seventeen. But I should add
that although patients may come to you under a burden
of guilt they stay with you only if you give them hope and
encouragement and implement it by curing them. Of course,

you might say that as a private practitioner of venereology I trade on people's moral frailty; it's a common enough accusation by unthinking people. But in fact no real doctor is medically interested in moral attitudes. It's the venereal diseases themselves I'm interested in, not the fact that they are associated with promiscuous living and the sexual organs. If syphilis and gonorrhoea were virus infections spread by invisible organisms in the air around us there wouldn't be the slightest moral obloquy attached to them, but they'd be just as interesting as diseases. So I made a reasonable amount of money from my private practice – this was all long before the days when the national health scheme had levelled all doctors to roughly the same income – but I had no time to spend it. During these years I never had a free week-end. I was on duty at St Martin's several days in the week sometimes from ten in the morning until ten at night, including some Saturdays, because if you want to get people to come to a clinic for treatment you've got to be there after normal working hours; and on Sundays or in the few brief hours I could squeeze from my responsibility as head of the department and senior medical officer I was seeing private patients or doing research. About all I ever had time for in the way of self-indulgence was a quarter of an hour's browse round a bookshop. I tell you, my dear chap, doctoring doesn't leave you time for mischief.'

That this was true was evident from the large number of his publications. These publications, which I had every chance of examining, were unfortunately far beyond my layman's comprehension because they included formulae and data that it would have taken me years to assimilate. But the startling thing about them was the clarity with which they proved that the Doctor seemed to have endless endurance. For in addition to stretching twenty-four-hour days to include the time for writing these papers he achieved another studious triumph. He became a doctor.

To explain this puzzling statement I must enlighten you to a greater extent about the recognized degrees in the medical profession. A student who earns his L.R.C.P. and M.R.C.S. is thereafter entitled, legally and ethically, to practise as a doctor. The degrees of Bachelor of Medicine or Bachelor of Surgery carry no more privileges ('There *is* no greater privilege than to cure the ill,' John Hunter said) but earn him extra professional esteem because they prove he has passed more advanced examinations. Strictly speaking, none of these degrees (all of which, as I've explained, the Doctor had early tacked on to his name) entitles him to be called Doctor. He's an authorized practitioner of the profession of medicine but not a Doctor by title. In ordinary parlance and correspondence, however, he is addressed as Doctor by his professional colleagues, there being something risible about the notion of being addressed as, for instance, 'Bachelor Smith'; and his patients, unaware of these fine distinctions, naturally call him Doctor too. But to become truly entitled to the prefix he must earn the degree of M.D. (Doctor of Medicine). This is the highest titular achievement in the profession, and the etiquette of it is, that, having hitherto been courteously addressed in correspondence as 'Dr' John Smith, he now drops the redundant prefix and becomes plain John Smith Esq., M.D. Everyone of course continues to address him verbally as Doctor, but if his addressors are his professional colleagues there's a new respect in their tone, for they're no longer being merely courteous – they're acknowledging his higher learning.

When next I saw the Doctor I asked him if he could fill in my record by conjuring up any details of the examination.

'Indeed yes,' he said. 'Every single one. But the complexity of the written papers would mean little except to another medical man' – he looked at me amusedly over his glasses – 'which you certainly aren't, judging by your struggles to master a few common medical simplicities. But I can explain a little of the human interest, as I think you writers call it. And that might be a bit more acceptable to lay readers.'

He paused in his characteristic way to straighten his narrative in his mind, and this time he stood by the window looking down into the street below. He was wearing a dark grey double-breasted suit of worsted cloth, slightly outmoded in style but none the less bearing the indefinable timelessness of all good tailoring, and he remarked on the change from his customary black coat and vest and striped trousers before telling me about his Doctorate of Medicine.

'Curious. I must subconsciously have known you were going to ask me about the M.D. today. This is the suit I wore— However, I'd better tell the tale properly or I shall muddle you.

'As you know, I was really anxious to take the M.S. degree; but when my plans were altered by my recall to St Martin's I substituted the M.D. as a target at the back of my mind. Venereal diseases, which had been the surgeon's province because of the continual use of hypodermics and scalpels in the treatment, had become more and more the province of the physician since the invention of Salvarsan, and I thought that as my path had been directed this way I might as well aim for the physician's M.D., which is the equivalent of the surgeon's M.S.

'I was constantly on the lookout for opportunities to sit for the exam., but, as you can guess, in those busy days there weren't any – or so it seemed. In practice, if you really want to do a thing you always squeeze the time from somewhere. And eventually, by cutting my sleep down to four hours a night, I did. This happened when, in course of time, another hospital – shall we call it St Swithin's? – asked me to reorganize its entire Venereal Diseases department. I left St Martin's in April and St Swithin's gave me three months for the reorganization. As you may imagine, I was busier than ever, so it seemed to be a good time to add to my bothers by swotting up for the M.D. I light-heartedly thought that it would be more of a challenge. It was, too. I'll spare you the details except to explain to you about the final exam. In this, you are taken to two hospital patients and told to make a diagnosis and prognosis in respect of each of them. You have no case histories or details of any kind; you start from scratch and the only information you're allowed is what you can find out from the patient himself (one of mine was a child, who couldn't help much). Both cases are chosen for their complexity and because many aspects of them are confusing and likely to lead you to make false diagnoses. You have three hours to examine your patients and write fully detailed papers giving your reasons for arriving at your diagnosis and prognosis, and suggesting treatment. This you do under the eye of an invigilator. I may say that it's quite a strain to write against time about cases of such complexity. In my case I found it so gruelling that my adrenals – they're the little glands that supply you with unsuspected energy to see you through crises – were completely exhausted and for three days I found it impossible to walk steadily or concentrate on anything I had to read.

'Well, you can imagine how anxious I got waiting for the result. If I failed, my new position as Director of the St Swithin's clinic certainly wouldn't be jeopardised, but failure wouldn't help my ego much – especially when I was lecturing to the students. It was to back up my self-esteem a bit that I ordered a new suit – this one – and I wore it on what I came to think of as "the fateful day".

'There was a tradition that before the full details of the examinations were published a preliminary notice bearing only the examination numbers of the passes would be posted up on a little board outside the Quadrangle of the College. On the date of this announcement – it was the twenty-fifth of July – I made my way down to the Square with very heavy footsteps. As I came in sight of the College my feet dragged even more. I could see a few people edge up to the board, look carefully at it, and move off without any sign of pleasure. I wondered if I too would be disappointed. Here was I, a mature man and as apprehensive as a child worrying about a junior scholarship. It seemed ridiculous, and I told myself it wasn't the end of the world even if I hadn't passed. But the funny thing is, that occasions like that *are* the making or breaking of one's own little world. Absolutely everything seems to depend on them. So you can imagine what sort of a turmoil was going on inside me as I approached the board. However, there it was – my number. But something else too – something I'd never dreamed was even faintly possible. Beside it, in brackets, "Gold Medal".'

The Doctor turned from the window and sat down on the sofa. He had counterfeited very ably the look of a stunned man. Even across all these years I caught something of his astonished pleasure.

'It's a very great distinction, you know. So great that I'd only vaguely heard of it. It isn't a thing you go in for, you see: it's just something that comes to you if your contribution to the science of Pure Medicine is – is – what's the word I want?'

'Brilliant?'

'That's it. It doesn't sound so conceited if you utter it.'

I believed the Gold Medal to be the imprimatur of medical success known of by the layman, who rarely encounters a doctor who has achieved it; and I asked the Doctor if I was right in my belief.

'That's the thing. It's cast from twenty golden sovereigns. Several doctors who've won it have sold it for its worth so that they could buy microscopes or other equipment, but I've never had to do that. It's a pretty bauble, isn't it?'

I acknowledged that it was and asked the Doctor how he'd celebrated its award.

'I didn't. Too busy. I sent off a telegram to my parents, who were in Southampton at the time, and got a bus back to St Swithin's. I had a wire back from my father the same afternoon, and if you'll wait a minute I'll find it for you.'

The wire was discovered without much ado under the blotting-pad (did he, I wonder, gain a little nostalgic pleasure from a quick glance at it in times of stress?) and when he showed it to me it proved to be exactly the sort of congratulation that any father might send to his son when that son had achieved one of the highest distinctions in medicine. It was neither sentimental nor rhetorical. It simply said that the Doctor had worked hard and deserved his success and that his father and mother sent their love. Putting it back under the blotting-pad, the Doctor said I might also like to see other messages he had had. He then found for me, and blew the dust off, a scrap-book containing messages of congratulation from members of the boards of governors of his two hospitals, the Dean of the St Martin's medical school, and innumerable medical colleagues. They were all most generous in their praise, but this generosity, the Doctor told me, had not been unmixed with malice from colder corners of the medical world. 'No: my achievement turned out to be subject to attacks of spite and jealousy too. You get this sort of thing in the doctoring business no less than in any other, doctors having the same variety of temperaments as other people. Administrators sometimes stand in your way and other doctors mutter darkly about you knowing too much – as if somehow you'd robbed them of their knowledge to increase your own. However, there were never any dramatic consequences of this professional jealousy. It was just something I learnt to endure. And it never grew to such an extent that it outbalanced the generous tributes that were paid to me by warmer people, or the enormous pleasure my parents' jubilation gave me. And of course after that I got a simple kind of joy out of being called "Doctor" and knowing that it wasn't just a courtesy title. I really was one: a Doctor of Medicine.'

# PART THREE

# The Doctor

# 11    *Phenomenal Activities*

The Doctor's progress through the colonnades of learning was rewarded by greater prizes than gold and approbation. His filing cabinets are conveniently stuffed with all manner of quotable evidence of medical activity; but the biggest cabinet of all is the one holding the case-histories of his patients. The challenges of venereal sickness and sexological problems over forty years have left a great drift of documentary evidence – 'And these of course are only my private patients,' he told me. 'The patients I've seen at St Martin's and St Swithin's are recorded there, not here, and are certainly many times this number.'

Except by going through each case-history individually – a task too daunting for either the Doctor or me – it would be impossible to determine which patients were cured and which not. And even such a detailed examination wouldn't necessarily tell everybody's full story. Not all patients follow advice or continue their visits. For reasons of their own they disappear into the blue, or become re-infected, or decide they know better than their doctors, and their histories are never fully documented. But that there must be countless triumphs against the enemy recorded in that cabinet is beyond doubt.

On New Year's Day 1964 it seemed to me apposite to ask the Doctor to switch to the other subject of his specialized field – sexology. Though the word can mean no more than the study of sex ('esp. among human beings', the dictionary adds carefully) it had never been quite clear to me what there is to study in sex *qua* sex. Perversions I knew about – as who doesn't? – but these seemed to me a field of study for the psychiatrist rather than the physician. Biological differences between men and women must have been exhausted as a study long before there were doctors to study them. The ignorance of sexual functions some people have, which the Doctor had already told me about, is clearly a social phenomenon having undertones of psychological insecurity, and the ignoramuses themselves wouldn't be very interesting once enlightened. So I was stuck in the dark as to the practical value of sexology. I asked the Doctor what the study of sex (esp. in human beings) meant in relation to actual patients.

'Why,' he said, 'it means, in the main, the study of sexual abnormalities of a physical nature. The perversions – you recall I told you about Celia and her transvestist friend Leslie – are usually psychiatric studies, though I'm often called in in an advisory capacity; but there are plenty of physical abnormalities.'

'You mean such as hermaphrodites?'

'Hermaphroditism is such a condition, of course, but extremely rare in humans. I've never come across a true herma-phrodite – and by a true hermaphrodite I mean a being born with both male and female reproductive organs fully developed – but what are commonly referred to as "sex change" cases are not so rare, and one or two of them have come my way. I'll tell you about them – though I can probably only add a few tech-nical details to what you already know, because they were sensa-tional newspaper stories at the time. And if you ask me how they became sensational when it's accepted by everybody that doctors keep their patients' identity as quiet as the grave, I can only tell you that that's your province rather than mine. How do journalists ever get hold of stories? Sometimes because they're ruthless and have no concern for anything or anybody except themselves or their own jobs; sometimes because they're genuinely fulfilling a public service by discovering something important or alarming or entertaining; sometimes because the people in the story are intent on broadcasting it for reasons of their own. You can decide for yourself which were the reasons in these cases.'

He began his usual rummage through the filing cabinet in search of the case-histories concerned and in a few minutes had refreshed his memory. Moving with his characteristic angular grace he came round the examination couch and perched himself on its edge.

'Looking for those two,' he continued, 'another name caught my eye – a case I found absorbingly interesting and was able to bring to a very satisfactory conclusion. And this one was by no means sensational so far as publicity was concerned. In fact there wasn't any publicity. It was just a case – like the thousand and one other cases tucked away in the box there. Nobody ever heard about it except other doctors, and of course one discusses cases with them without reference to names unless one is introducing the patient for specialist advice. And even after that you refer to them by symptomatic description rather than as individuals. "How's that Jacksonian epilepsy I sent you?" or "I need some help with that gonococcal Bartholin you asked me to look at" – that's the way we speak of people. Their names, though often famous, mean nothing. You may think it's coldly clinical, but their names and lives are never so interesting to me as their complaints except in so far as they're linked.

'Anyway, here was this man. He came into my ken first of all in a letter of congratulation from another doctor, who said how glad he was about my M.D. and Gold Medal and so on and then finished up with a request for advice.' The Doctor looked down at a letter he'd fixed to the case-history card with a paper-clip. ' "I have a miserable and very shy friend," he read out, "who was raked in the perinaeum during the war. Now married and can only get a fleeting erection – not enough to penetrate – can you suggest anything?" ' Looking at me over his glasses he added : 'All right. Now you want to know what a perinaeum is. Well, it's the area, roughly lozenge-shaped, between the scrotum and the buttocks. The nerves and muscles surrounding it have a lot to do with the control of both the anal canal and the genital organs; so if they're damaged – as in this case they were by a bullet – it may well be difficult or impossible to get an erection of the penis because of nervous or muscular deficiency. Clear ?'

I said it was clear.

'Right. Now a bullet damaging the perinaeum might also have damaged the testicles or their associated parts and thereby prevented the manufacture of semen, so the first thing to be established was whether the patient could in fact make sperms. One way to do this is to massage the prostate gland, which induces a seminal flow, and that was the way I did it. There *was* a seminal flow, but it was of very meagre quantity and took a long time to emerge. As I'd suspected, there'd been some damage in the testicular area too. So we had two problems: the difficulty of erection and the tardy flow of semen. (The actual quantity didn't matter.) They were overcome in the simplest and most obvious way – though like many simple and obvious things it took a great deal of thinking about. I had a splint made to fit the penis and instructed the patient how to fix it as soon as he achieved his erection by normal stimulus. So although not remaining erect by its own volition, so to speak, the splint would enable the penis to penetrate. His wife had to give a lot more co-operation than is normally necessary because of the delay in ejaculation. But this she did very willingly – she was a woman who desperately wanted a child – and didn't even mind that she and the husband had to remain in a state of coitus for two hours before a satisfactory ejaculation was achieved. But it *was* achieved and the result was a perfectly normal baby. So there, you see, is one sort of problem the sexologist is faced with.'

Having disposed of the unfortunately injured man's record card as matter-of-factly as I'm sure he approached the problem, the Doctor extracted a couple more cards from the file and sat down again – this time in the armchair opposite me with a card on each chair-arm and his glasses balanced on his knee.

'These were the so-called "sensations". They both came my way in the same year and you could ferret out their names from the newspaper files. I hope you won't, though. They've had enough publicity in their time and no doubt want to be left in decent obscurity now.'

I told the Doctor I wanted no more than the facts.

'Right. Well, the facts in the first case were these. I was called
in to give expert advice in a legal action for an annulment of
marriage. The husband was petitioning on the grounds that it
wasn't possible to consummate the marriage because his wife
wasn't a complete woman. She wasn't, either. As you know,
there are basic organs common to both sexes – we all have heart,
liver, brain, lungs, kidneys and so on, of course. But there are
also reproductive and genitive organs that are common to both
sexes, though normally in a rudimentary sense in one or the
other. The breasts and nipples are the most obvious; both sexes
have them, but the woman's are much more developed. The
ovaries in the woman are homologous with the testicles in the
man, though in neither sex should these particular genital organs
be rudimentary : they must be fully developed in both man and
woman for children to be conceived of a union. The growth of
pubic hair is equally developed in both sexes, too, but in the
woman takes on the pattern of a triangle with its base uppermost, while the triangle of the male pubic hair grows with its
apex toward the navel. The clitoris in the woman is homologous
with the man's penis, both being capable of erection by erotic
stimulation; but the clitoris is of course much smaller and
normally concealed by the fold of the inner and outer lips, or
labia, of the vagina – which, by the way, correspond to the
scrotum in the man. The development of all these organs – and
of the general structure, muscular development, and so on – of
sexually different bodies as a whole is controlled by hormones,
which are the organic product of the living cells – though they
can also be manufactured chemically.

'This girl I was called in to pronounce on had developed
abnormally because of an abnormal distribution of the hormonal
cells. By the time she was sixteen she had no more than vestigial
ovaries and breasts, but at the same time had a very over-
developed clitoris and similarly over-developed labia. Her neck,
thighs, hands, and teeth were also masculine in construction,
though her hair, voice, complexion and waist were feminine. Of
course it was impossible for her to conceive because of the under-

developed ovaries, but she got married all the same and she and her husband adopted a baby. But the sexual frustrations were too much for the husband and after four years he petitioned for a nullity decree on the grounds that it was impossible to consummate the marriage because his wife wasn't a true woman. It was that question I had to advise the court on. When I'd been into her case history, examined her clinically, and discovered that she'd had a couple of operations and hormone treatment to help eradicate her masculine characteristics, I came to the conclusion that she had the mentality and instincts of a woman but that she could never be a complete wife. So the petition for annulment was granted. All the same, she got married again later. And what did her the most good was knowing that she was seventy-five per cent woman anyway. Imagine what an emotional disturbance must be set up by being uncertain of your own sex. As you see, she writes about it here.' The Doctor unclipped a newspaper clipping from one of the record cards and I read : 'A famous sexologist has told me that I have always been predominantly female and always will be . . . I have never been so happy . . . but I am not going to appeal against the nullity of my marriage. I do not want to go through the courts again. The Judge at the nullity hearing quoted a doctor that my "general appearance is inconsistent with what one usually finds in a girl", and the next day a newspaper headline read "Wife Is Man Again" and the story was told of how I had had the operation. I had been frightened after those reports to go back [to work]. As I walked in I felt everyone's eyes on me, heard everyone whispering. One older woman left a bunch of girls to come up and say, "Tell us all about it." It was a horrible experience. I decided to see this leading sexologist. [He] rates me, to be exact, a three-quarter woman. But that satisfies me. No longer need I ask myself, "What am I?" . . . What of the future? . . . Will I fall in love again? All I can say is that I want to be a wife with a husband, a home, and perhaps an adopted child.' Beside this typically sensational declaration was a picture of a tall slim girl wearing shorts, a very feminine sweater, and high-heeled sandals.

The retoucher had done a good job in shading the heavy face, and the girl looked, as the caption said she was – 'never so happy'. But it seemed to me that any human being so scurvily treated by nature would have to get along very largely without normal happiness. As the Doctor said, the emotional disturbance caused by the deviation of one's sexual pattern would be considerable; but my own view was that it was unlikely to be much improved by knowing that you were 'three-quarters woman'. The Doctor, however, corrected me on this. 'It was the uncertainty of knowing whether her masculine characteristics were going to develop still further that was her main emotional trouble,' he said. 'But with the surgery that had already been performed and the hormone treatment I prescribed she was reassured on that score. And she is, as I say, now living a normal female life except in the one respect of being unable to conceive. That, of course, is always a sad disability, whatever the reason for it may be – and it accounts for a great many of my sexological cases. Barrenness in women and impotence in men can be caused by a number of things – all of them much more common than that case I've just been telling you about. One of the commonest, as you now know, is venereal infection; and that's why venereology and sexology are so closely allied. But I'm not going into the simpler cases of infertility while I've got this other case still to tell you about.'

The other case was certainly a very famous one and was, in a way, a reversal of the one he'd just told me about. The patient was born male, and indeed became aggressively male in all his activities. He played tough football, had a strong bent for mechanical things, and engaged in several fields of activity regarded as especially masculine : he married and fathered two children, fought in the army and the Royal Air Force and became a prisoner-of-war, and ran an engineering business. Then began changes in his physique followed by changes in his instincts and mental outlook, which took a feminine turn. One manifestation of this change was his increasing fondness for feminine clothing and for the asexual companionship of women,

which his wife, not unnaturally, interpreted as marital unfaith-
fulness. A drift toward transvestism is rare so late in life – the
patient was then in his thirties – and at whatever age it takes
place is commonly rooted in psychological causes and unaccom-
panied by physical changes. The usual transvestite, in fact, is
dependent (as Leslie was) on the 'props' – the wigs, clothing,
and so on – to achieve the temporary conviction that he is of the
opposite sex; his wishful thinking doesn't promote any biological
change. But in this particular case there was a marked biological
change – progressive atrophy of the male pudendum, swelling of
the breasts – and a consequent rather than a causal psychological change. He sought the advice of several doctors, including
an endocrinologist who believed the change to be due to a mal-
formation of endocrine glands controlling the hormonal secre-
tions that determine and preserve the sexual balance. This
specialist's prognosis was that the change was undoubtedly progressive and that it would be much better for the patient if it
were speeded up – any attempt to retard or reverse it being in
his opinion hopeless. The speeding up was accomplished by
hormone treatment, but a considerable amount of plastic
surgery was necessary to complete the metamorphosis. The
buttocks, waist, and breasts, for example, could all be plastically
assisted to simulate the metamorphosis into a female.

The Doctor was called upon to give a sexological report on
this unusual case and subsequently he assisted the late Sir Harold
Gillies, who carried out the plastic surgery.

'The main problem in this case,' he said when he'd outlined
the general details, 'was one of . . . well, I suppose you might say
a problem of finality. I agreed with the endocrinologist that
the metamorphosis couldn't be stopped or reversed; and there
was nothing very difficult about the surgery that would give the
patient a more feminine physique – slimmer waist and so on
(though we couldn't slim the ankles down, because the girth's
dependent on the bone structure). But you see, there was no
absolute certainty that the metamorphosis would *remain* complete. It was possible that the glandular trouble would right

itself – go into reverse – and a de-metamorphosis set in. If that should happen the patient might as desperately want to be a man again as he then wanted to be a woman; and the absence of the genitalia could cause a profound psychological disturbance. I had long discussions with Harold Gillies and assisted him at the actual operation. It was quite a tricky one.'

Veronica broke into his technical description of the operation by arriving with the tray of tea at that moment. It was dusk outside now and, just as it had seemed apt to broach his New Year's Day conversation with a suggestion of a new subject, it seemed right to close it by catching at something I hadn't been able to fit into what was at the time a more important conversation. 'You were saying before Christmas,' I reminded him, 'that there was a ghost story.'

'Indeed yes, I remember. There are also a couple of examples of what I can only call telepathy. And, like my dream of Rhuddlan Castle, they puzzle me. My scientific mind being out of key with my extra-sensory mind, they puzzle me very much indeed. But the facts are clear enough – dates, times, chapter and verse. Only the explanation is missing. And I think we simply have to accept that "there are more things in heaven and earth" et cetera. Not a scientifically acceptable proposition at all. However—'

He settled into his chair, leaving all the lights on so that there shouldn't be any suggestion of the gathering dusk providing 'atmosphere' to influence his narrative. I could see he felt the harsh light of reality to be a far more valuable property.

'Here you are, then: the facts. In August, nineteen-twenty-one, I spent my summer holiday in Scotland with my family and a few friends. We left on Sunday the twenty-eighth of August to motor leisurely back to London, and by Wednesday the thirty-first we had reached Knutsford, a little market town in Cheshire, and we decided to stay the night at the hotel there. We were all cheerful as we sat down to dinner, including me. I had no worries on my mind and was physically very fit and well rested after a month's holiday. We started dinner at eight and

I was about half-way through my soup when I experienced a most extraordinary sensation. I felt intensely cold all over and could hardly talk or move, let alone finish my soup. I hadn't any nausea, headache, or pain: I simply felt as if I was being forced to remain attentively silent, listening. Then someone at the table said, "What's wrong with the Doctor? Look how pale he's gone. Give him some brandy." I found it awfully difficult to speak at all, but I managed to convey that I didn't want any brandy, I just felt that I was involved in something terrible that was happening somewhere, and that everyone must get on with dinner and let me be. I looked at my watch. It was ten past eight. I just sat on there at the table unable to move or speak any more, becoming completely oblivious to everything that was being said and going on around me. All the strength seemed to have been sapped out of me and I remained like that for twenty minutes, when the strange feeling of anxiety and immobility passed abruptly. I finished my dinner and slept soundly. Next day we carried on to London and did the two hundred or so miles in the one day. All the time I was driving I was wondering what tragedy I had been briefly caught up in the night before. But I had no clue.

'The next day I anxiously went round to my surgery to open my post. But there seemed to be nothing amiss: nothing even faintly disagreeable, let alone tragic. I couldn't dismiss the incident from my mind even though I felt very fit, but no news to tie up with it came until the following Monday, September the fifth. Then I got a letter from my father. This told me he was coming to London to attend the burial service of an old family friend, a Mr Joseph Wilson.

'This Mr Wilson was an ardent church worker and was on several boards and committees. He was a picture dealer and colourist by profession and had a shop in Oxford Street and a home in Trinity Road, Wandsworth. He had been a very close crony of my grandfather and father and was also very fond of me and had always taken a great interest in my career. The manner of his death was this: On the previous Wednesday –

the thirty-first of August, the day of my inexplicable experience at dinner – he'd left his shop at eight o'clock to go home and had been knocked down by a bus as he crossed the road. While the ambulance was taking him to hospital he continually asked for me by name. But once in hospital he became unconscious and died soon after half-past eight.

'Now: are you going to tell me that the date and time were coincidental? I'm not convinced. But nor can I explain what mysterious power or mechanism it was that woke my consciousness. Wilson could have had no knowledge of my location – we hadn't known ourselves until just before dinner that we were going to stop at Knutsford, and I certainly hadn't seen him for several years. How can a person in pain, half conscious and very well aware of being near death, send a message to a conscious mind two hundred miles away? How were the vibrations directed at me? I don't know, and I can see you don't either.'

I agreed that I didn't know and added that I thought people knew a sight too much anyway and that before long, with their pokings and probings they'd probably discover the ultimate mystery of life itself, so that there wouldn't be any purpose in living it to find out what it was all about.

'Not a very scientific view,' the Doctor said; 'but I see what you mean. Now then: will you have the ghost story next or would you prefer the other odd example of the working of the non-scientific mind?'

I said I'd settle for the ghost story as a filling for what we might call a kind of telepathic sandwich.

'Right. In that case you need listen no more. It's all set down in Kenneth Walker's book *The Unconscious Mind* and I've got a copy here.' He rang the bell for Veronica and when she came he asked her to fetch the book for him. 'You'll find it in the little room across the corridor,' he told her, 'right of the window, on the shelf with a pile of Medical Directories. A paperback.' When Veronica returned with the book he opened it at the right page and handed it to me. I glanced through it and then said, somewhat ungratefully, that I'd prefer him to tell me the story himself. Mr Walker's presentation was perfection itself, but I preferred a version with the rough edges still on. He looked rather pleased and, with his thumbs in the armholes of his waistcoat, told me the story. I've left it intact save for subbing out conversational hesitations and prolixities and references that might establish his identity.

'One beautiful sunny morning in April, nineteen-thirty-eight, I left my consulting-room for St Martin's, where I was due to lecture to the students in the school medical theatre for an hour from twelve o'clock midday. I'd seen several patients during the morning, felt very well, had had a good breakfast, had no cold or temperature, and was not particularly worried about anything. In fact, all was well with me and my world. I wasn't hurried, and as I went along I cogitated quietly and complaisantly about the points of my lecture, for I always looked forward with pleasure to my hour's talk to about ninety senior students. It was about ten minutes to twelve when I walked into the hospital through the casualty entrance and along the main corridor to the medical school. As I passed the big ward in Block Seven to go out into the open-air part of the corridor which is flanked on each side with stone pillars supporting the building overhead, a nurse came out from Block Eight and walked toward me. The distance from the seventh to the eighth block is about thirty yards. The sun shone across the cement floor of the corridor and cast the shadows of the pillars at regular intervals along the passage from right to left, for the sun was shining from the right-hand side. There was no one else in the corridor as we walked toward each other; our positions were such that we were equidistant from the two blocks so would pass each other halfway between them. As we approached each other I had my eyes on her, and, although I didn't recognize her, I followed the hospital custom and, as I was wearing a hat, when she was about two yards in front of me ready to pass on my left, I took it off to her. But as she passed me she disappeared before my eyes. I found myself alone in the corridor.

'I had noticed that her dress and cap were rather old

fashioned, but it was certainly a St Martin's regulation dress
except that at the shoulders it was puffed out instead of lying
flat on the figure. Her face was well defined with clean-cut features and her expression was placid and normal in colour and
gradation. Her movements were natural and she had all the
appearance of being a person of normal flesh and blood. She
threw a shadow and I could have sketched her likeness or recognized her from a photograph. Had she passed by me and not
disappeared in front of me I should have called her a normal
person. There was nothing startling or frightening about this
apparition – if you like to call her by such a name – for there
was nothing menacing about her actions or countenance, and she
appeared just as solid as you or me. It seemed to happen so
naturally that it caused me no apprehension or alarm – just
astonishment.'

The Doctor registered a parody of astonishment – he became
a child knowing it is expected to look surprised because its parent
has hidden round the next corner and jumped out saying 'Bo!'
Then, chuckling at the success of his impression, he continued
his story in a lower key.

'Unperturbed, I walked on to the school and for the moment
thought no more about this strange happening. I gave my lecture
and then had a modest lunch at the Students' Club. After lunch
I thought again how strange it was for one of the nurses to disappear before my eyes, so about a quarter of an hour before
the afternoon's work began at two o'clock I went to the Matron's
office to tell her. She wasn't there, but the Assistant Matron was.
She stopped me half-way through my tale and said that I had
undoubtedly seen the Block Eight ghost. I replied that it was
extraordinary that though I'd been at St Martin's for so many
years I'd never heard of it, especially as I'd worked continuously
on the top floor and in the basement of that particular block.
She told me that that was because they had had so much trouble
with the nurses who had seen it, and some nurses had refused
to do night duty in Block Eight on that account, so that the
matter was kept very quiet and seldom spoken about. I asked

whether there was any story attached to the ghost and she answered that there was. It was said to be the ghost of a nurse who had worked in the top ward of Block Eight who had quarrelled with her ward sister in the 'eighties of last century and who, in a fit of pique, had thrown herself over the balcony and killed herself.

'That was the story. But what had happened to me? And why? Did it really happen or was it an hallucination on my part? What did it mean? Had it any particular significance for me personally. Was it a portent to me individually, a warning of some strange or disastrous event about to overtake me or my family? I asked myself these questions and thought about them for many months without satisfaction. I was naturally sceptical about all supra-normal manifestations. Moreover, by temperament I was equable and thoughtful, somewhat self-possessed and matter-of-fact rather than excitable and demonstrative. As I passed along the corridor daily I continually sought an explanation, especially from the scientific point of view of this intriguing occurrence, for I knew that what I've described without the slightest distortion or exaggeration undoubtedly did happen out in the open air on that sunny day in April. Had I seen some reflection from a glass window or other bright reflecting surface? There were no such objects anywhere within range. Had I taken any drug, eaten or drunk anything which may have affected me? Maybe some type of catalyst had accelerated my chemical and physical processes and caused my normal limitations of vision to overstep their boundaries so that for a while I was able to perceive additional wavelengths beyond the normal ken of eyesight? The answer to all these suppositions was simply No. So hallucination can be ruled out. If I could solve the problem I might be able to condition myself for the experience to be repeated, which I was most anxious to do. How could I prepare myself so that I would be able again to perceive with those wavelengths of light which have been proved scientifically to exist but which we are normally unable to use? I could find no answer.

'The war came. Some time during its second or third year the Secretary of the hospital told me that on the previous day he'd been conducting a journalist round the hospital. This journalist was writing an article about the fire-fighting arrangements, and had been shown our organization, which included two voluntary spotters keeping vigil on the top floor of each of the main blocks. When they reached the top of the eighth block the Secretary commented on the difficulty they had in keeping the spotters there because it was haunted. The journalist asked whether anyone had seen the ghost and the Secretary told him yes, that I had, and that it had also been seen by the Assistant Clerk of Works. I pricked up my ears when I heard that the Assistant Clerk of Works had seen it too, for of course I knew him and knew that he was a quiet, unassuming, and sincere man not given to tarradiddles or hallucinations any more than I was. As I was sleeping at the hospital at that time I asked him next morning at breakfast whether he'd tell me about his vision of the ghost so that I could compare it with my own experience. He not only told me but also wrote a statement which he signed and which I still have.'

'And which,' I said, 'I've no doubt that you can find in a couple of shakes.'

The Doctor smiled and put his glasses on. 'Oh yes. I can find most things in one or other of these lucky dips – and that, after all, is the point of a filing system.'

Sure enough, the Assistant Clerk of Works' statement came to light in a few seconds. It read :

'In the summertime of 1934, between five and six o'clock in the evening, I was walking along the open-air part of the main corridor of the hospital, when I saw a nurse who immediately attracted my attention because she looked so old-fashioned, wearing as she was an extremely long skirt and an old-fashioned cap. I remarked to my companion, the Clerk of Works, on the peculiar nature of her dress. He looked rather oddly at me and said that he could not see the nurse I was talking about; in fact, he implied there was no one in the corridor. At this point the nurse reached the Block Eight Nurses' Home and to my astonishment completely disappeared. We examined the only door close to where she disappeared, which was firmly locked, being a Night Nurses' Home. The only thing I noticed about her features was that she appeared to be distressed : otherwise she seemed to be a perfectly normal person. She was walking along with quick steps. It was then for the first time that I had ever learned of the existence of the Block Eight ghost, about which my companion, the Clerk of Works, told me.'

The Doctor slipped the statement back in its envelope. 'As you see, his view of the ghost corresponded very closely with mine, though a period of four years separated them. It's also worth noting, I think, that the apparition made both him and me respond to its presence with an action – his to check on whether the nearby door was locked, mine to raise my hat as to a real person; and for both of us it disappeared in the same place. Although at the Matron's request, I avoided talk about the ghost while I was in the hospital – she had difficulty enough as it was in getting nurses to do night duty in Block Eight – I did mention it to a Cambridge professor – Stratton by name – who was closely connected with the Psychical Research Society and whom I met on some social occasion. He was most interested and asked me if he could deposit both the Assistant Clerk's statement and mine in the Society's archives. So there you are,' he concluded as he rose to answer the telephone. 'I'm immortalized in the archives of an important society.'*

---

* It is worth noting that a friend of mine was motoring down to the West Country one day and gave a lift to a girl who turned out to be a nurse from St Martin's. I had been telling my friend the Doctor's ghost story and he asked the nurse if she'd ever heard of the Block Eight ghost. She had indeed. It was a benevolent ghost, she said, and prevented the nurses making mistakes when administering treatment or medicines. 'It's the ghost of a nurse who in the last century gave a patient a fatal dose of something by mistake and afterwards committed suicide. Now she's around all the time. I personally have had a syringe inexplicably knocked from my hand three times when I've made mistakes in the dosage, and other nurses have had the same thing happen to them.' She said nothing about actually seeing the ghost, but referred to it as 'a powerful force that grips your arm or shoulder at the moment when you're about to do some damage.'

The telephone conversationalist this time was a gentleman speaking from Tokio. 'The marvels of science,' the Doctor said with schoolboyish glee. 'Via Oslo – clear as a bell. Here it is, Wednesday. We made an appointment for Saturday half the world away.' He rubbed his hands together. 'Marvellous. Science. Yes, marvellous indeed. Travel; conversation; disease; it eases them all.'

'Ah,' I reminded him, 'but it doesn't explain everything. Your other psychic experiences, for instance.'

'Oh, that. Yes. I'd forgotten I hadn't told you the third of my stories. But this is really an experience I was in on the edge of, so to speak, and I doubt you'll think it's much more than an odd coincidence.'

I told him that it didn't matter what I thought; I was merely an intermediary reporting the facts. He then went on to tell me how, when he was on another of his several trips to Cambridge, where he visited friends and made his round of the bookshops, he had made a number of purchases of books he'd taken a fancy to, including a beautifully bound copy of Carlyle's *French Revolution*. During his absence from London he had lent his flat to an old friend who had been staying there with another lady, a friend of hers called Mrs Alice Tate. When the Doctor arrived back he found the flat empty. A note from the Doctor's friend explained that she and Mrs Tate had gone to hear a noted spiritualist and clairvoyant who was giving a lecture at Wigmore Hall and that they would be back shortly. The Doctor unpacked his suitcase and decided to give the Carlyle to his friend to acknowledge her kindness in looking after his flat during his absence. The two ladies returned. They could scarcely wait to tell him of their experience with the clairvoyant. It was clear that they were excited and baffled, and although the Doctor immediately presented the Carlyle to his friend she, for the moment, no more than thanked him and put the book on a table without looking at its title. They had, she said, had a truly remarkable afternoon. The clairvoyant had gone into a trance-like state and, on emerging from it, had said to the audience that he had a message for someone named Alice. The two ladies had nudged one another, but Mrs Tate had been too shy, and perhaps too sceptical, to reveal her own name even when the clairvoyant had appealed for a response. 'I have a message for someone named Alice in this audience', he said again and was obviously puzzled that no one responded. He repeated the challenge once more and when there was still no response decided to give the message anyway. 'The message for Alice,' he said, 'is from someone named Mary. She wishes to tell Alice that she is sorry for all the trouble she caused but that she did not know what she was doing and she is quite happy now.' What further astonished the two ladies was this : Mrs Tate had had a relative named Mary who had suffered considerable emotional distress and as a result of this had committed suicide. She lived in a house on the edge of a lake and one night when she had gone to bed and was reading, her desperation had simply overcome her, she had put down her book and walked straight out of the french windows across the lawn in the moonlight, down to the lake. And she had gone on walking until the water submerged her. 'Was it any wonder,' the two ladies asked the Doctor,' that we were astonished? Neither of us had ever seen this clairvoyant in our lives, and he couldn't possibly have known us or anything about us.' But they were even more astonished a moment later when, discussing this strange occurrence, Mrs Tate revealed in passing that the book Mary had been reading on the night of her suicide was Carlyle's *French Revolution*.

'Now I can't claim,' the Doctor said, 'that I experienced any special inducement to buy that particular book – not beyond its material beauty, that is. It was just a good binding I admired and wanted. Nor did I have any particular reason for choosing that one rather than several others equally pleasing to give to my friend. In any case I bought it a full fortnight before I returned to my London flat. And you can, as I said, put the whole incident down to coincidence, which certainly has a very long arm. But I think it's worth recording as one of several odd happenings that are quite impossible to resolve by the scientific methods I'm used to. And with that,' he added, 'I shall scoop you out of the consulting-room and go and get myself ready for a dinner of the Royal College of Physicians, which, incidentally, you might like to enlighten your readers about in a short paragraph.'

Which is easily done. The College was founded in 1518 by Thomas Linacre, one of Henry VIII's doctors, who, with the help of Wolsey, got the king to grant letters patent for the founding of a society that would keep quacks out of the profession. Licentiateship and Membership of the College are of course by examination and their attainment is one of the conditions of being allowed to practise medicine in England; but Fellowship is by unanimous invitation of all Fellows present at the annual election. The Fellows form the governing body of the College and must forfeit certain practical advantages on being elected – they are no longer allowed, for example, to dispense their own medicines, or indulge in business activities such as keeping a shop, or employ an assistant.

We left the building together and walked the short distance to his home, where he would bathe and change and make his way on to the College. I had to make a journey of a different kind, back along the Doctor's lineage, which is a good deal more complex than the lineage of the College, and about five hundred years older.

# 12  *A Long Way Back*

I find the fascination of family pedigrees as such somewhat limited. All that splendidly illuminated calligraphy is good to look at, but it tells one nothing about the people except that they were married and had children, plus poignant little terminations to branch lines that read 'all ob. inf.' The Doctor's pedigree is longer than most: it goes back to the ninth century, and the escutcheons that illuminate it are famous. Some time ago he spent all the spare moments of a whole year preparing a genealogical chart to be copied by heraldic artists and calligraphers for occasional reference. The chart was done with black and coloured inks in miniscule handwriting on sheets of squared paper hinged together. When opened out it stretched for nearly fifteen feet and, like the filing cabinet full of case-histories, displayed a daunting number of names. Bewildered, I traced lines until I was dizzy but understandably added nothing to my knowledge of people like King Alfred and the Black Prince – both of whom were forebears of his – and remained totally ignorant about the unknowns. I decided that once again the Doctor would have to be my guide if any of them were to come to life and illuminate his heritage. When next I saw him I arbitrarily pointed to a branch headed 'Duncombe, Earl Feversham, of Duncombe Park' and irreverently asked him, 'What about this lot?'

'My mother's side,' he said, kneeling on the floor with the appropriate bit of the chart unfurled and the rest of it held down by convenient chair legs. With a silver paper-knife he prodded at names and dates and, figuratively speaking, put his distaff ancestors into clothes and houses and surrounded them for me with happenings

'Right at the beginning, in the middle of the sixteenth century, there was this Thomas Duncombe, who married a wife called Joane and lived in a house called Barleyend, which is in the parish of Ivingho, near Tring, in Hertfordshire. He also inherited a place called Stocks, in Aldbury, nearby. A Georgian house, itself called Stocks, was built in the eighteenth century, and this, or one of the farmhouses belonging to it, was the home of my mother's family until nineteen-thirty-four, when it was bought by some rich Americans and sold to a syndicate, who in turn sold it for a girls' school. Stocks had twenty-two bedrooms and stood in three hundred and seventy acres with some marvellous views. Mrs Humphrey Ward the novelist lived there at one time. She leased it from Sir Edward Grey, the Foreign Secretary we had some conversation about at your club that night, and he inherited it from a Mrs Gordon, widow of a great friend of Sir Walter Scott's. Scott stayed there many a time and adapted the name of Ivingho village into the title for his novel *Ivanhoe.*'

I remarked that Stocks seemed to have a lot of subsidiary owners or lessees and asked how that had come about if it belonged to the Duncombes.

'Yes, you're right to ask about that,' the Doctor said, 'because the answer reveals a dastardly deed or two.' He traced some lines for a moment and then pointed to another ancestor. 'Now this one, this David Duncombe who lived from seventeen-eighty-three to eighteen-forty-three, was a great crony of the Earl of Bridgwater, whose estate joined his. Bridgwater was a covetous villain who wanted to get the Barleyend house and land and join it to his own. In the matter of coveting land he had no principles at all, and even went so far as to encroach on some of the common land belonging to the people of Berkhamsted, nearby. To get Barleyend for himself he played cards with David Duncombe every night, got him so drunk that he didn't know what he was doing, and gradually won from him everything he possessed – Stocks, Barleyend, money, everything. The shock killed David, but Bridgwater had no mercy and wouldn't even allow the widow and her children to live in a cottage on the estate. He banished them all to Eaton Bray in the next county, Bedfordshire, so that they couldn't spread the news of his misdeeds around Hertfordshire. And to make certain that none of the sons should take their revenge on him he forced them into the army and navy. One of them, also named David, was with Wellington at Waterloo and led such a charmed life carrying despatches between the regiments – he had three horses shot from under him – that Wellington told him, "The bullet isn't made that will hurt you today." He was romantic as well as fortunate, and when he returned from the war and found that his sweetheart, a girl called Ann Smith, had jilted him and was about to put up the banns and marry someone else, he mounted his horse and rode at a terrifying speed over to Tring, where he arrived just in time to stop the banns and seize Ann for himself – which he apparently did without any objection from her. They lived happily ever after and had one child, Mary Ann Duncombe – this one here, see – who was born in eighteen-twenty-five and was my grandmother. A marvellous woman : she had eleven children and lived to be ninety-three, had good eyesight and hearing, and hadn't a grey hair in her head. Her memory and powers of concentration were remarkable right up to the time of her death, and she was very fond of telling the story of how the wicked Earl of Bridgwater had been punished for his treatment of her grandfather. The story was this : just after he had seized the Duncombe estates he was enjoying his ill-gotten gains by riding along Duncombe Terrace, a fine avenue of beech trees, and there he saw an old woman gathering firewood at the side of the road. Like so many bad types, he couldn't bear to loosen his grip on anything that belonged to him, and he immediately rode over to the old woman, thrashed her with his riding whip, and threatened to send her to court for stealing his wood. But he met his match. The old woman upped and cursed him there and then. She swore that no son or direct heir of his should ever inherit the estates, for all sons should die before they were twenty-one. The curse has been fulfilled, too. The Earl's son was thrown from his horse and killed before he was twenty-one and since then no son has inherited. The estates went to a nephew and then to another nephew who hadn't enough money to maintain them, so had to sell; and that's why there have been so many owners. When the syndicate put it up for sale in nineteen-thirty-four I thought of buying it back into the family, but the price was thirty-three thousand pounds and I certainly couldn't afford that.'

The telephone rang and the Doctor straightened up from his kneeling position in a single swift movement and without the slightest sign of a squeak or groan at the back of the knees, and within seconds was involved in a highly technical conversation with a colleague on the subject of the removal of a patient's spleen. With his free hand he dipped into the filing cabinet and found the case-history card and without hesitation reeled off a series of suggestions in answer to the questions his colleague was putting to him. Had I been the patient I should have felt well on the road to recovery by the time he put down the phone. But he didn't let that distract him from genealogical matters. I had been about to ask him how the Earl of Feversham came to be at the head of the Duncombe family, but he forestalled my question.

'The Duncombes – or at least one branch of them – came to be Fevershams in seventeen-forty-seven, when Anthony Duncombe, son of another Anthony Duncombe who was governor of Scarborough Castle, was created Lord Feversham. The third baron was created an Earl in eighteen-sixty-eight, and the present Earl is *his* great-grandson and is married to the Earl of Halifax's daughter. Duncombe Park, the Feversham family seat, is in Yorkshire. The house was designed mainly by Vanbrugh, and it has Ionic temples and rotundas, and a marvellous terrace walk which gives you a succession of quite different pictures of the countryside as you move along it. It proves that in those days, when people designed for the future, they had wonderful vision, for they must have been relying in their designs on effects that might take fifty to a hundred years to materialize but which in

fact turned out exactly as they'd envisaged them before the trees
and other features of the design had grown to their full
maturity.' The Doctor said 'Marvellous' again – making the
word a small additional adornment of his enthusiasm for the
eighteenth-century gentleman who built great houses and parks
with such a finely attuned eye for the future. Before he could
prod any more with his paper-knife the phone rang again, and
this time, when he'd answered it, he asked me if I'd leave the
consulting-room – 'But don't go away: it's a lady who hasn't got
an appointment, says she doesn't want to see me professionally,
and won't keep me more than ten minutes. I'm curious: her
voice seems familiar but I can't place it, and she won't give her
name.'

I slipped out to the waiting-room and read a long article on
Georgian silver in *The Connoisseur*. Veronica came in before
I'd reached the end to tell me the Doctor was ready for me
again.

'Interesting,' he said as I re-entered the consulting-room. 'You
remember I said her voice on the phone was faintly familiar? It
turned out to be a woman I hadn't seen for over forty years, so
her familiarity must have been faint indeed. But I did remember
her as soon as she told me what she'd come for and reminded me
of the circumstances.'

'An old patient,' I said.

'Not in the sense you mean, no. But she was brought round
to St Martin's one dreadful winter night in nineteen-twenty.
There was a storm blowing and it was bitterly cold and this
wretched little girl – she couldn't have been more than sixteen or
seventeen – was brought in by a policeman. He'd seen her trying
to kill herself by hurling herself into the river and had stopped
her just in time. He left her with me and I tried to get her to
tell me all her troubles; but she wouldn't, she was in that stage
of desperation that all suicides reach – her mind was un-
balanced and she needed sympathy and treatment. I told her
this – that she was desperately ill and must be treated and that
now she must stay so that she could be properly looked after at

St Martin's – but she said that was useless, that she felt so ill and wretched that if all I could offer her was hospital treatment she'd go back to the river and "finish with everything". I told her, "I wouldn't if I were you. The water's so cold. It's such a beastly windy night too", and for some reason this mild reproach persuaded her and she allowed me to take her to one of the wards and put her in the hands of the sister and nurses. They humoured her, gave her a sedative, and put her to bed, and by the morning she was ready to begin a course of psychiatric treatment that eventually cured her. She came today to tell me how successful this had been and how kindly they'd treated her at the hospital. In the end she'd completely regained her confidence and married a good chap whose business had prospered and now lives comfortably and happily. Also – and I think this is the nicest "thank-you" she could have given me – she persuaded her son to take up medicine, as a thank offering, she said, for those few mild words about the wintry night and the cold water; and apparently he'd actually been one of my own students. This was the reason why she still wouldn't tell me her name – she'd never told her son about the suicide attempt, hadn't wanted him to have any undue sympathy from me, and still preferred him to be anonymous so far as I was concerned even now he'd qualified as a doctor. Now isn't that the sort of story that belongs in books? Forty years pass and she comes to thank me for saving her life.' The Doctor laughed. 'However, it was my past we were going into when that pleasant interruption came.'

I remarked that it had appeared to me to be a past liberally chequered with kings and queens and top people.

'Top people and bottom people and middle people in great variety,' he said. 'In a burst of enthusiasm one week-end I counted the names on this pedigree and there are over a thousand of them on the male line of descent alone.' He looked at me over his glasses, and added, 'I take it neither you nor your readers would want to hear something of all of them? No, I thought not. We'll just pick out a few of the more interesting ones, then.'

He traced back a couple of generations and paused at his paternal grandmother, a girl called Anne Jane, who was born in 1825 – 'A girl of great character and spirit. She actually eloped – and with a distinguished minister, too. Her parents refused to let her marry her sweetheart so they simply took the next coach to London and were married there. She had tiny feet, which she was very vain about, and said they'd been ruined by the cobbled streets of London and that she'd had to wear a size larger in shoes ever since her visit. She and her husband returned to the bosom of the family and were forgiven by her father, who was something of a character too. As you see, his first name was Watkin and he was a merchant. He left thirty thousand pounds when he died in eighteen-seventy-six at Wrexham, in north Wales, where he'd been in business all his life. He retired from business once and went to live in Pwllheli, having handed over the reins to Anne Jane's half brother, Evan, a waster who nearly ruined the business before dying of drink at the age of forty-seven. Old Watkin had to rush back to Wrexham, pull the business up by the boot-straps, so to speak, and retire for the second time when he'd done it. His other daughter, Mary, married a man called Evan Evans, who was the sixth son of a sixth son, and they had six children, of whom one was the commodore of the Canadian Pacific shipping line and was nicknamed "The Gorilla" on account of his physical strength. Another was this one on the chart here – Mary Catherine Evans. She fell in love with Robert Armstrong-Jones, Lord Snowdon's grandfather, when he was a medical student at Bart's, but they had a lovers' tiff just before she sailed from Liverpool to New York in eighteen-eighty-two, and although she hoped to make the quarrel up when she returned a year later she never in fact did make it up. The ship she went to America in, the *Abyssinia*, ran into a terrible storm and was lost for sixteen days. There were seven Mormons on board and they were all trying to make converts to their faith when the storm struck the ship. Mary said that as soon as the ship was in difficulties the Mormons forgot all about their conversions and went dotty. They lay about on the floor, swooning and swearing and generally exhibiting all the signs of terror, while Mary went calmly on playing the piano.'

I was so enchanted by the picture the Doctor's résumé conjured up for me, of his Aunt Mary playing (almost certainly) Mendelssohn's 'Songs Without Words' in the saloon of the storm-battered *Abyssinia* while the sweating Mormons lay about and groaned in anguish, that I paid scant attention to a generation or two as he prodded with his paper-knife back along the lines to the beginning of the seventeenth century, where there was one of a number of decorations to the chart – this one a small inset picture of a rather jolly looking cleric wearing a mitre on his head and a bandolier across his cassock and having a sword slung at his side and a rifle on his shoulder. This was John, of the Williams family, joined by marriage with the Doctor's own in the eighteenth century and taking its name from the whim of one William ap William ap Gruffyd or Cochwillan, who shortened his cumbersome designation to the simpler form in the sixteenth century. 'John Williams,' the Doctor told me, 'had a sad accident when he was seven years old. He lived in Conway, where there's a castle on the seashore. He and his friends were playing there one day and jumping from the castle wall to the beach below. They were trying a primitive form of flying – leaping off the wall and letting the strong wind get under their voluminous coats so that they sailed gently to the ground. Apparently the wind wasn't enough to support John when he jumped, and he fell across a groyne, permanently damaging his genitalia. His biographer said he was "chaste perforce, a stranger to wanton lusts", but that didn't stop him entering the Church. He became Bishop of Lincoln and afterwards Archbishop of York, and probably if King Charles had trusted him instead of the Archbishop of Canterbury, Laud, there wouldn't have been a civil war. As it was, he was a royalist who became a Roundhead and was, as you see by this picture, militant in favour of both causes. He was imprisoned both by the Star Chamber and by parliament. He had a nephew, Sir Robert Williams, who inherited his estate, which eventually passed to Anne Williams, a woman of very dubious reputation indeed. She was supposed to be, and probably was, the wealthiest heiress in north Wales. She was one of Queen Caroline's ladies-in-waiting and the Duke of Cumberland's mistress. She was wildly extravagant and had great matrimonial troubles, both of her marriages to two Irish cousins named Prendergast coming adrift. She died in poverty and her one-time estates were the subject of endless litigation. Her home, a mansion at Pant Glas, was sold and partly reconstructed, and what was left of it was bashed to the ground in a great storm in seventeen-ninety. And that was the end of poor Anne and all that was hers.'

While we were hovering round the civil war period he pointed out to me another ancestor of his who was High Sheriff of Merioneth in 1650 and who had been fined £1,200 for lending the King £300 when he was penniless and fleeing from the Roundheads. This bold royalist, whose name was Robert, was the custodian of William Prynne when he was moved from prison in Caernarvon Castle to prison in Jersey in 1637. (Prynne was, of course, the commonwealth pamphleteer who was sentenced by the Star Chamber to have his ears cut off for animadverting against cosmetics and theatrical performances.) Robert's father, William, was also High Sheriff of Merioneth, and later of Caernarvonshire, and a great man for public affairs. He was a great man for his own affairs too, and was shrewd enough to marry a wealthy heiress from Montgomeryshire, Elizabeth Herbert, and to see that his children also married wealth. Robert, William, and their forebears, derived directly from Morris ap John ap Meredydd of Rhiwaedog, a notable squire whose ancestral line went plumb back to Gruffyd ap Cynan, Prince of Gwynedd and chief of the first royal tribe of Wales in the eleventh century. Gruffyd married a girl called Angharad, who was directly descended from Sihtric Gale, the Norse king of Dublin, Man, and the Isles of Scotland, and their son Owen was grandfather of the first prince of a more or less united Wales, Llewelyn Fawr, who brought the English royal line into the family by marrying Joan, the natural daughter of

King John. From John there is a line of twenty-two sovereigns stretching back to Alfred the Great, and before him there were Ethelwulf and Egbert. Egbert died in 839, and I remarked to the Doctor that it must be rather pleasing to be able to trace one's ancestry such a long way back.

'We all go a long way back,' he said. 'We can't all trace the journey, that's all. I've found it an absorbing activity being an amateur genealogist. I don't know that there's any special virtue in being descended from Kings. Like most other people, some of them were good, some not. But there's a great deal of pleasure – for me anyway – in filling in gaps in one's ancestral line. I like ferreting about in family papers, parish registers, cemeteries, records of old buildings and so on. When Princess Margaret married Tony Armstrong-Jones I did another bit of research and discovered that he has a dual descent from my own family. His father is a tenth cousin of mine through a marriage into my family back in the eighteenth century; and his grandfather, Sir Robert Armstrong-Jones was also fairly closely related to us on his mother's side. My grandmother's sister Mary – the one who went to America with the Mormons – was the girl who wanted to marry Sir Robert, you remember, and had the lovers' tiff and never married him at all. If she had, Sir Robert would have become a great-uncle of mine by marriage and the two families would have been even more closely related than they are.'

Although the long journey back through eleven hundred years of the doctor's ancestry had been telescoped into an hour, and we had paused to look at fewer than a dozen of his progenitors– and those not very closely – it seemed to me that in that brisk look I had at least spotted a possible explanation of his odd telepathies and precognitions. The Celts have always been known to be a fey people. Eleven hundred years of their blood must fairly pickle a man in poetic and visionary qualities. I was in a way surprised that he didn't revisit medieval castles every night in his dreams, that he wasn't constantly feeling apprehensive of death two hundred miles away, encountering ghosts in corridors in broad daylight, or lighting on the bedside reading of suicides. Somewhere back along the line, beyond the yeomen, the mariners, and the merchants, I had no doubt there was an alchemist or a wizard (a lively wizard at that) who had pondered and incanted over a crucible in the same way that centuries later the Doctor was to peer into test tubes of odd mixtures; who had cast spells for lovers and removed warts by charms, spirited enemies away, raised phantoms to haunt the wicked. These mystic talents, I thought, probably ran in some degree in the blood of all of us. Why shouldn't the Doctor have some share of them in the form of second sight or telepathic communication? I put this notion to him and he accepted it and said my reference to visionary qualities reminded him of yet another occasion when he'd experienced a precognitive glimpse of coming events. Naturally I asked him for the story.

'Well, this was during the war when the enemy had been very active with his bombing raids and a peaceful night almost anywhere in England was the exception rather than the rule. When the late day and dusk were uneventful you couldn't somehow bring yourself to believe that the night to come might well be your last. Wishful thinking no doubt, but you felt that peace was the reality and war a grim fiction.

'It was this sort of evening when I left the hospital to walk home to dinner. I'd had a hectic day and the air seemed fresh and stimulating even though it was in fact filled with the fumes of city traffic. The sky was ... serene ... serene – yes, that's the word I want – and you could look up and see the silhouettes of the buildings very black against it. No foreboding there, just a city getting ready for night. Pleasant in its way if you stopped to look and take it in – which I did. In fact I turned off down a side street where the traffic was thinner and I could enjoy the pleasant feeling a bit more quietly.

'Then I had this odd feeling that I ought to return to the hospital at once. You know how it is? Rather that feeling you get when you've forgotten something and can't even remember

what it is you've forgotten. I stopped and went through my
pockets, but everything was there, and when I mentally checked
up on the day there didn't seem to be anything I'd left undone.
I walked on, but the compulsive feeling that I must return became even stronger. And suddenly I knew without question
why it was that I must go back. The hospital was going to be
bombed.

'You might of course say that there was nothing remarkable
about such a hunch. Any place was likely to be bombed at any
time. The fact that the evening was at the moment tranquil was
no guide at all. Planes could approach and acres of a huge city
be laid waste in half an hour or so. But surely the rational thing
to want to do if you took your hunch as an accurate forecast
would be to get away from the scene of possible disaster as
quickly as possible, self preservation being one of the strongest
of the human instincts'.

'Well', I said in the tone in which one signals a profound
remark, 'your instinct might have been right and your rationalization of it wrong. I mean, your hunch might have been a bit
out geographically. Perhaps the bomb you foresaw was going
to fall on the place you were standing on when you foresaw it
and your urge to go back to the hospital was simply your instinct
telling you to get out of the way'.

'That could be, of course. Or you could take the whole thing
a step further and say that both instinct and rationalization
were wrong and that fate was simply playing an ironic game
with me by tricking me into returning to the hospital to get out
of the way only to get me there at the moment the bombs began
to fall.'

The Doctor could outdo me in profundity any time.

'Anyway,' he went on, edging me back on to the track of facts,
'the thing was that I had this overwhelming compulsion to
return, plus a strong visual representation in my mind of my
own department turned into a heap of rubble. And although
I knew there was absolutely nothing I could do about it –
nothing to stop the bombs falling and nothing to save anything

if they did fall – I turned round and went straight back to the hospital.

'Nothing was changed since the half hour I'd left the place. It wouldn't be, would it? The department was there – all the equipment in the right places – the benches, the sinks, the syringes, the sterilizers, the photographic stuff, the microscopes. All just as I'd left it. Being a scientist, I'm no sentimentalist; all the same, I thought of that line of Walter de la Mare's, "Look thy last on all things lovely" – you know? Nothing lovely to look at in the aesthetic sense; but I looked, fixed it in my mind. Then I left the place and walked home – not lingeringly, but quickly, ready for my dinner and thinking no more at all about bombs or anything else disastrous.

'I slept well – never knew another thing until the phone bell woke me early in the morning. It was the Registrar. "Your department's finished", he said. "Not a thing you can do about it, I'm afraid. Bombed. Just completely laid waste. I thought I'd better tell you quickly, get the shock over with".

'I told him it wasn't such a shock as he might think. Then I dressed and went down to the hospital. It was a heap of rubble all right – just as I'd seen it in that glimpse the night before. The bomb had evidently fallen more or less exactly on the spot where I'd seen that ghostly nurse disappear before the war.

'And that's about it. What on earth was the *use* of my flash of precognition?'

I said I didn't know, but that it was just as well he wasn't living in the days when witches and warlocks were hunted for having prophetic visions or he might have been flayed in the courtyard of whatever happened to be the handiest version of the Tower of London. And that reminded him that he nearly *had* been shoved into the Tower once. It was getting late, but I couldn't bring myself to pick up my traps and go without discovering what startling circumstances had brought the Doctor within reach of the Yeoman Warders.

'The circumstances weren't at all startling,' he said. 'That was the point, really. They were apparently the most ordinary circumstances in the world. It was the woman involved and the manner of her involvement that were startling.

'The woman I mean was in my own profession, so to speak – in medicine, or on the fringe of it. She was a hospital almoner – not at one of my own hospitals – and of course had the job of interviewing hundreds of patients and deciding about them from the administrative point of view. She became a patient of mine and asked me to try and do something about a chronic backache which pained her almost continually. I found this backache was due to a misplaced womb and I corrected it without much trouble, though very occasionally spasms of pain would recur and she'd have to come back to me for manipulative treatment.

'This was at the beginning of the last war. At the end of nineteen-forty-one she came to me to say goodbye as she was going away. Naturally I was surprised and asked her why she was giving up hospital work, and she said quite unemotionally that she was going to Germany. I thought she was making some sort of joke I couldn't see the point of and shrugged, waiting for the explanation. But the explanation simply was that she *was* going to Germany – as a spy! She was going to be dropped by parachute too. Well, you could have knocked me down with a feather, as they say – or even without one. She just didn't look the type. She was perfectly ordinary – well built, medium height, with a pleasant but quite undistinguished face, and you couldn't for a moment imagine her being dropped into enemy territory as a spy. I say "you couldn't for a moment imagine". That's wrong, of course. When I did begin to use my imagination I realized that it was just because of her undistinguished looks that she was good spy material. I asked her how she'd ever become involved in such adventurous work and she told me that it had all begun long before the war when she had answered an advertisement asking for picture postcards and photographs of Germany.

'I wished her luck and off she went to be literally dropped into the war. I didn't hear of her again for nine months, when she rang me up and asked for another appointment. When she

came she told me she'd had an exciting time and was going back
again but that this time it would be more dangerous. She was
one of a group of six of our people who had been involved in the
killing of a German secret agent and they believed they were all
marked for doom as soon as they returned. In the circumstances,
she said, there didn't seem much point in having her back done;
but she was going to have it done all the same as there
was always a chance. I was full of admiration for the courage
she showed in her light-hearted approach, wished her well and
watched from the window there as she crossed the road and went
down into the underground – it seemed a very suitable place for
her to disappear into.

'I was delighted when about six months later I heard her
voice once again on the phone and she asked for another
appointment for more treatment. When she came I congratu-
lated her on her survival, and although this time she was cagey
about her future activities it was enough for me to know that
she'd come through all right so far.

'A few days later, at midday, I was going to fetch my car
from the garage where it was being serviced. I walked on the east
side of the road and just before crossing encountered my patient.
I raised my hat and asked her if her back felt better; but to my
astonishment she completely ignored me and passed by. Apart
from the fact that she didn't disappear before my eyes it was
rather like a meeting with another ghost. But I just shrugged
and went on across the road to the garage. People always have
reasons for their actions and I didn't feel resentful in any way.

'Next morning she phoned to apologize for her behaviour and
said she must come and explain. I told her that was quite unnecessary, but she insisted on coming. She came, and as she
walked in through the door there her first words were, "You
very nearly upset the entire apple-cart yesterday." Naturally I
wanted to know what apple-cart she was talking about and she
told me that at noon she'd arranged to meet a very high-ranking
German secret agent on the very spot where I'd encountered her
and raised my hat. She was the only person in Britain who could

identify him, so it had been arranged that whoever spoke to her at noon should be arrested. It was only her quick wit in refusing to recognize me that had saved my bacon. She told me that as I approached her there were two detectives a step or two behind me, a police car parked at the kerb, and a couple more detectives and another car on the opposite side of the road. Fortunately she ignored me completely and managed to convey by her in-difference to me that I wasn't the wanted man. Otherwise I should have been pushed quickly into the car and driven off. I suppose I shouldn't have had much trouble about identifying myself, but the point was that my capture would have left her high and dry when the real spy came along. There wouldn't have been anybody there to arrest him, and the whole plan would have gone awry. Naturally I asked if they got the man and she said yes, within half a minute he'd come along, spoken to her and been arrested, and was being whisked away to the Tower of London – "Where you'd have been if you'd insisted on speaking to me", she added. Now what do you think of that? – all those goings-on in Baker Street in broad daylight and me knowing nothing at all about it. I'd have given a lot to see it all happen. Why on earth didn't I turn round? The things that go on un-noticed more or less under your nose are always surprising when you learn about them, don't you think?'

Surprising indeed. But – not to resist a platitude – the whole of life is surprising. It isn't irrelevant to the Doctor's story to tell you that I remember once walking through Stepney late at night and finding myself surprised that the tales I'd heard tell of that part of London were true. In those days I was naïve enough not to believe anything unless I saw it for myself, and I'd gone to see and, as my informants said, 'collect a giggle'. I saw, all right, but I didn't giggle. I need mention only a couple of Stepney's street entertainments on that particular evening. One was a bevy of three street whores all of whom were taking their customers in adjacent doorways that were warmed and faintly illuminated by the light of a watchman's brazier. (The name of W. W.

Jacobs crossed my mind. Poor man : he didn't deserve such wildly improbable consideration.) It was a cold night and possibly the warmth was part of the primitive comfort offered in lieu of a roof and a bed. I suspect it was more likely that the faint illumination was necessary for the women to make sure they weren't being given foreign or counterfeit coins. (One of them had a box with a slit in the top into which she dropped the coins after inspecting them. The fee seemed to be fourpence if I calculated the number of coin falls right.) The customers stood leaning against the walls – one of them fumbling anxiously with his flies and commenting obscenely on the slowness of the man ahead of him when he was still second in the queue from the doorway. The women found it necessary to drop their skirts to settle the finances of each transaction before beginning, but apart from that they kept them tucked up with an absurd resemblance to respectable ladies venturing into the sea for a paddle. Considering this bit of observed social history years later, I did not find it hard to believe the Doctor's information, retailed by Stefan and Daniel, that their (and Hitler's) venereally infectious whore, Hannah, operated in the Nordwestbahnhof doorways at the equivalent of threepence per customer, four or more to the hour.

The other surprising sight I saw that night was through a steamy café window. Inside, an 'entertainment' was going on. Some tables had been pushed together to form a 'stage' and on these three sodomites were coupled, in tandem, in a state of bestial coitus. An enthusiastic audience was indulging in orgiastic revels of its own, and on the wall opposite the window, I recall, was a showcard which advertised 'Magic Gipsy Ointment for Bad Feet'.

Both these scenes were at once ludicrous and sad; and both were observed by a good many witnesses beside myself. But bystanders – including children – were giving them scant attention. Too used to them, no doubt.

Not unnaturally, these squalid goings-on imprinted themselves very clearly on my mind. But the war came, and I supposed that, with the extensive bombing that destroyed so much of the east end of London, the squalor had been ground under the heel of death. But in 1961 the priest of a Stepney church, St Paul's, Dock Street, told the London Diocesan Conference of Churchmen, 'We have developed into an area of low-level café-clubs for drugs, drink, gambling, and women. We have a hotbed of vice on gutter level. Humans are like rats, living in filth, four in a bed. We have actually been exhibited to sightseers in this setting. One day a coach pulled into Ensign Street. They had an American guide; he led them to a Somali café-club. "You'll find everything here", he shouted – and indeed they would. At the same spot, one evening, before the Street Offences Act, I found a group of my schoolchildren with coloured adults watching a coloured man and a white girl having sexual intercourse. People who know only West London prostitution know nothing of prostitution on the sordid and vicious level of Stepney. Girls screaming and fighting for their money, girls taking man after man in the open street, girls being smashed to the ground by men, thrown down bodily and kicked. There are people I know personally who saw three men committing sodomy in the open in Wellclose Square. One Stepney street has been a row of brothels for years. In October the roofs were taken off, but the brothels continued in lower rooms.'

The relevance to the Doctor's story of these observations of the priest's and mine is of course that they illuminate, very harshly, one reason for the illimitability of his battlefield.

# 13  *A View of the Battlefield*

Had I been a symbolist I should probably have tried to express the illimitability of that battlefield by writing of a waste land, endless and gloomy, characterized by the stunted growths of symbolic *spirochaeta* trees and craggy formations of symbolic *gonococcus* rocks; these would have had symbolic clutching feelers and their shadows would have been veined with symbolic human vascular systems. In the middle of this odd set-up would be the tiny lone figure of the Doctor, soldiering on with his symbolic little black bag and his symbolic test tube filled with wild *spirochaetae* beating with puny fists against the glass walls.

Mercifully, I am not that kind of writer. But the battlefield is boundless all right, if not quite a waste land. There is no country in the world populated by promiscuous human beings where venereal diseases don't have a chance to flourish. 'Promiscuous' derives from Latin words that mean 'forward' and 'to mix'. And since the human race is everlastingly going forward (whatever cynical doubts you may have) and, of necessity, everlastingly mixing, there are not likely to be any boundaries erected round the battlefield in the foreseeable future. Social customs like marriage, and the moral precepts of religions and civilizations, all tend, of course, to impose limitations to promiscuity; but, as you saw in that spotlight I briefly turned on Stepney, the barriers are easily crushed. And though the Stepney scenes appeared to be especially sordid because they were so public, you may be sure that the same sort of thing goes on, sometimes rather less publicly, in Mayfair. And in Seattle and Hamburg. And Macao and Nairobi. Tangier and Minehead, *et al*.

There, then, is the battlefield: everywhere. We can all look down on it. Far too many of us do, alas, in the snobbish sense of that phrase. The scene becomes obscured by euphemisms, distorted by revulsive shudders – except by the medical profession, which at least tries to cure and count the injured. The British Office of Health Economics, an organization sponsored by drug manufacturers, says in a published report that in 1961 there were 37,100 new cases of gonorrhoea, in 1962, 35,400; and of syphilis there were 3,820 in 1961 and 4,120 in 1962 – all in Britain. And in France – to go no further abroad – the Academy of Medicine was told at the end of 1963 'there is a marked increase [in syphilis] in a number of areas, the worst being Saint-Etienne. A number of other towns, including Nancy, Dijon, and Rennes, are not far behind'. And a congress of the World Health Organization in Stockholm was told that 'Europe's economic integration has helped to create a common market in venereal disease . . . There are now about thirty to forty thousand new cases of syphilis in Europe every year, and three hundred thousand to four hundred thousand new cases of gonorrhoea. These are just reported cases. Actual incidence rates are considered to be much higher.' The Office of Health Economics began its report with the frail admonition, 'The diseases would vanish within a few decades if promiscuity ceased.' And it went on to say, *inter alia*, 'The rise in new infections among males is an exception to the general pattern and might well be attributed to infection through homosexual contact. [Also] the rise in travel abroad and the use of immigrant labour have increased the risk of contracting the diseases. What is needed,' the report ended with remarkable lack of originality, 'is a drive to educate the people to the dangers of V.D.'

What is needed, rather, is more bite in the drives that are made. The occasional poster campaigns, press advertisements, and warnings displayed in public lavatories are a limp reminder that venereal diseases exist; but none of them has the powerful effect that, for example, the satire of Hogarth had in the eighteenth century. Hogarth's 'The Harlot's Progress', a moral tract in six engraved scenes, was as popular then as a popular television show is today, but its effect on the Gin Lane shenani-

gans of the London of the time (which equalled in flagrancy
those of the 1962 Stepney I've just mentioned but were rather
wider spread) was made through the bitterness of the artist's
satire rather than his mocking appeal to the moral sense. The
fifth engraving in the series, for instance, shows the dying harlot
sitting by the fire in her sordid room and is sometimes accompanied by a textual commentary to interpret the satire to later
audiences : 'Released from Bridewell, we now see her in all the
extremity of penury and wretchedness, dying of the malady
which so frequently accompanies her profession. The two quacks,
whose injudicious treatment has probably accelerated her death,
are quarrelling about the efficacy of their nostrums, and each
accusing the other with having poisoned her. While the maid-
servant is calling to them to cease quarrelling and assist her
dying mistress, the nurse is plundering her trunk of the few poor
remains of former grandeur. On the floor lies a paper inscribed
*Anodyne necklace,* at that time deemed a sort of *Charm* against
the disorders incident to syphilis; and on the table a paper of
Dr Rock's pills. In this pitiable situation, without a single friend
to close her dying eyes, or soften her sufferings by a tributary
tear; forlorn! – destitute! – desolate! – and deserted – the
heroine of this eventful history expires; her premature death
brought on by a licentious life, seven years of which have been
devoted to debauchery and dissipation, and attended by consequent infamy, misery, and disease. The whole story forms a
valuable lesson to the young and inexperienced, and proves this
great, this important truth, that a *deviation from virtue, is a
departure from happiness.*' An equally biting satirist working in
the medium of television today might well teach a more
'valuable lesson to the young and inexperienced' than any of the
hortative but uninformative 'Beware of V.D.' advertisements
or the lists of addresses of V.D. clinics posted in public lavatories
– which are useful only after you've caught the disease.

Taking my view of the battlefield to the Doctor for his critical
examination on an early spring day in 1964, I realized I had
worked myself up into a fine state of indignation about unneces-

THE DOCTOR 207

sary woeful ignorance, lack of governmental interest, et cetera. I was composing sermons, preaching, becoming a high and mighty bore. I rang the Doctor up and asked for a later appointment and spent the afternoon slashing three thousand words out of my advice to the world in general on what to do about venereal diseases. I left in the script what you've just read, which seemed to be reasonably sensible and restrained, and kept my later appointment.

'Yes,' he said, 'a satirist might make an effect. I have my doubts, though. This isn't an age of satire and invective in the same way that the seventeenth and eighteenth centuries were, is it? Where are your Pope, your Swift, your Hogarth? And if they were here what could they do? The laws of slander and libel have tightened the screws on their kind of effective malice. However, you could be right. I think a great deal more might be done in schools to clarify the muddled thinking that always goes on around venereal diseases. It seems to be impossible to dissociate V.D. from sin and guilt and morality. As you've shown so effectively, V.D. is inextricably linked with promiscuity, and promiscuity is sinful according to our morality – a linkage which as a moral person I strongly support. But as a scientist I can only point out once more that it's pure chance that venereal diseases are sexual diseases. And if you take a society in which promiscuity is as moral as restraint is in ours – or, rather, if you *could* take such a society; for I don't think one actually exists, except, possibly, to the extent that polygamy is allowed – then you'd find that venereal diseases were wider spread but neither more nor less vicious in their effects. In other words, *spirochæta pallida* is indifferent to the so-called morals of human beings and bores his way from one into the other simply because the opportunity is given him by way of the one act that is necessary to propagate the human species and the erotic stimulus that introduces that act. Clearly it's impossible to stamp out promiscuity; and as I think I've mentioned before, if we medicos managed to invent an effective prophylactic our invention would only get snarled up in the sin-and-morality complex again : we should be accused of giving a licence for fornication – just as people who advocated birth control were, and still are for that matter. With anything sexual it's impossible to separate the desirable elements from the undesirable ones. So, one way and another, eradicating V.D. by preventive methods seems to be out – though a lot might be done by insisting on blood tests for immigrants and for couples about to be married, which happens in a lot of the American states. Controlling it by effective treatment is of course the other way to neutralize its dangers. But it's still true to say that even treatment isn't entirely free from moral censure, because there are those who believe – however covertly – that the disease is a punishment for transgression and that to cure it rather than to prevent it by complete continence is another licence for fornication. However, the Doctor's business is curing, not censuring. And there, I think, the medical profession itself needs a lot of education.'

For a moment the Doctor paused in his characteristic way, marshalling up his arguments with all the precision of a man programming a computer. I had become accustomed to these summarizing sessions and didn't attempt to speed them up or allow myself to wonder if I had run a subject into a cul-de-sac on an overdrive of unwarranted enthusiasm. Relaxing in the armchair I let my glance traverse the room and take in once more the familiar features, the reproduction of 'Rain, Steam, and Speed', the injunction to remember that No Two Cases Are Alike, the leaning towers of *Lancets,* the adjustable bed with its levers, the stethoscope hanging on the hook under the grey homburg hat, and the drug cupboard over the sink. Quite irrelevantly it struck me that all the time I had been visiting him, the tap, in need of whatever taps need in the way of maintenance, had dripped persistently. Till now I had never noticed it. Entranced, presumably, by my venture into the Doctor's extensive world, I had been unaware of an accompaniment that in my own miniature world of desk, pen, and intractable words would have driven me dotty. The knowledge closed in upon me that this was my last visit. It was saddening knowledge. A writer must everlastingly be closing doors on old worlds and prising open doors leading to new ones. He sees all of them with the eye of imagination – an eye bright or beady, according to his quality; but always an eye that sets things in perspective, selecting and discarding words, phrases, incidents so that the reader, he continually prays, is engaged. And as a book closes there is always the dreadful element of doubt, the thought of having chosen, from a million possible ways of writing about a man and his work – all of which have impinged, with the ferocity of hot irons, on his consciousness during his lonely tussle with words grasped singly from an over-heady plethora – at least nine hundred thousand of the wrong ones. Fortunately I have always slunk back from this suicidal bypath in time. And anyway at the moment I had something to slink back for : the Doctor was resuming his commentary on the needs of his non-specializing colleagues for education.

'You see, there are great difficulties. Most people who are suspicious that they've picked up a dose of V.D. are extremely reluctant to go to the family doctor. Part of the reason for this reluctance is of course the necessary revelation of guilt to a man they know, which adds up to humiliation; the other part is a vague fear that the knowledge will seep out locally. So of course they pop into a public lavatory, note the address of a V.D. clinic that isn't in their own district – that's another desperate attempt to maintain secrecy – and go there. So the ordinary general practitioner has very little chance of seeing a V.D. case. He might see a couple a year. And when he does, his over-confidence in a single shot of penicillin – probably the wrong sort of penicillin anyway – leads him to despatch a patient as cured when that patient may be very far from being cured. It's a hope-for-the-best policy, and you can't altogether blame the G.P. for adopting it. As you've discovered during your talks with me, the effectiveness of penicillin and the sulpha drugs has had a lot of over-emphasis. Experts like me aren't sure even now of the long-term effectiveness of penicillin cures; but for some reason or other this uncertainty has filtered through to the ordinary doctor without the reservations and doubts – in reverse, so to speak. Also, to carry out proper tests – the Wassermann reaction and so on – needs equipment that very few doctors possess, so that means getting in touch with the nearest hospital laboratory and all the paraphernalia of samples and delays. You can't altogether blame a busy doctor with three thousand patients on his books, a waiting-room full of depressing little illnesses and accidents, and babies to deliver night and day, for treating somewhat cavalierly an apparently simple case of gonorrhoea and mistaking it for husband's clap; or failing to remember that a gonorrhoea case may also be a case of combined gonorrhoea and syphilis. There's another angle too. I remember before the war there was a general practitioner who lived in a district where there was a lot of V.D. Many cases came to him and he began to specialize a bit. Then word got round that he treated V.D.; his ordinary patients stopped going to him. They were sniffy about sitting next to "immoral" people and unwarrantably afraid of "picking things up" as they called it. So in some cases it doesn't do to specialize. But all the same I think many doctors might take a bit more interest and at least pass possible V.D. cases to the nearest clinic.'

He had been sitting beside me on the sofa, and now he rose and moved in his loping angular way round to the door, which had just had a letter pushed under it. Stripping the envelope the Doctor revealed an impressive invitation card. He laid it on the desk. 'Well, that's a good thing : an invitation from this firm that makes scientific machinery to examine a new electron microscope that's about to be turned out on a commercial basis – a much more convenient job than the huge things that need physicists to operate them and as much space as you could put half a dozen hospital beds in. It's said to have even more remarkable powers of magnification too – magnifying many thousands of times rather than a few hundreds. Promising, I think. I wonder what more it'll reveal of my enemy?'

I remarked, with the best of intentions, that there didn't seem to be much more to learn.

'Nonsense,' the Doctor said; and his tone was the nearest to irritability I had heard. 'I haven't any false modesty and I don't mind saying outright that I have tried to learn as much as any man in the world about venereal diseases. I also know that I know remarkably little compared with what there is to be known. People inventing electron microscopes, people messing about in laboratories, people being curious about this and that in test tubes – that's the way everything's revealed.' He took his glasses from his pocket and polished them, the gesture like a paragraph mark to indicate a change of subject, for when he went on he had clearly forgotten his irritability and was probing his reminiscent vein again.

'I had a patient with a syphilitic umbilicus the other day,' he said. 'The *spirochaetes* had settled themselves there in her navel, making a horrid running sore of it. Queer in a way; symbolic somehow. I had to cut the navel right out, patch it up with a bit of plastic surgery. The girl was furious, so was her mother. They said a girl without a navel looked as if she hadn't been born properly. I did the right thing, though, cutting it out. You can't please all the people all the time. They don't please me all the time either' – the Doctor was in full spate again now and I settled myself back on the sofa once more. 'When I was attending as consultant venereologist at St Martin's I remember being in the clinic one day when two youths came in. Louts, they were, rather than youths. They sat there with their hats on reading comics and with cigarettes in the corners of their mouths and it was some time before I realized that one was the boss lout and the other a henchman of some kind; and it was the henchman who was supposed to do all the answering of questions. When I asked, for instance, if the boss lout had had intercourse with anyone, the henchman lout replied on his behalf. He sat there with the fag-end still at the corner of his mouth and said, "Intercourse? He's had more pokes than he's had meals." Of course that made me chuckle; but it's not really the way to go on. Another patient I had that same day, I remember, was a priest in some monastic order – you know – robe, girdle, sandals, tonsure. But when he stripped he was simply crawling with body lice. After I'd examined him he had to be disinfected. "Cleanliness next to Godliness?" I asked him rather pointedly; but he explained to me that in this case filth was a penance, like lying on a bed of nails. He hadn't had a bath during the whole of his monastic career – if that's what you call it. I could well believe it. He went into a convent hospital and I visited him there. Two nuns stood at the head of his bed, motionless and unsmiling as two guardsmen. But as I approached for my examination they whipped back the covers from top to bottom and there he lay, naked. There wasn't anything circumspect about them, as there is about the nurses in our hospitals – you know, revealing just as much of the patient's body as the doctor needs, keeping everything else concealed decently. They were perhaps showing their disgust that a monk of their order should be venereally infected. Nothing unusual there, though : Popes have had it, as you know. The sins of the flesh are common on this battlefield. Maybe his penance of filth was imposed on him in the first place for getting what is generally accepted – especially among the religious – as a filthy disease.' He glanced at his watch. 'How I do go on. I must stop. Not for your sake – you appear, as always, to be interested – but because I have work to do. And I expect you have too.'

I said Yes, I had. And with that I took my leave of the Doctor.

But not to forget him. I went to the Club and ate a solitary dinner, getting the waiter to dissect my grilled sole. Then I went up to the library and stood at the Edward Grey window. It was a clear night and I did not hear, as the Doctor had heard, the ghostly battalions marching to the Somme. I heard instead his voice, chuckling as he told me about his father :

'He always carried a little chamois bag on a string round his neck. He put a tenth of his income into it, and that was to be given to anyone in need.'

Or about old men with prostate trouble :

'They have difficulty passing their water, you know – often have to use a catheter, a rubber tube to pass into the urinary tract, and if they're businessmen they carry these catheters coiled up in their bowler hats.'

Or about his student days :

'You do your dissecting on dead bodies that had been pumped full of formalin. And in your bed-sitter where you studied you had a box of bones – a complete set, all the bones of the human body – which you bought for three pounds. I had a human brain too – that cost a pound. Where did all the bodies and the bones and the brains come from? South America mostly : it was a flourishing export trade with them. Then came the day when all the dissecting was done, you went round the wards with the doctors, listening to them and desperately trying to answer their questions. Then suddenly you were a doctor your-self and you hung a stethoscope round your neck and fingered it with great pride. That sort of pride soon passes : you keep the stethoscope under your coat, clipped to your braces, out of sight.'

When I think of him now I shall think of his undeviating con-versation – one subject, one bit of narrative, all of it relevant. Pause. Question. The assembling of his thoughts. Then another narrative. I shall think of him as old enough to be wise and young enough to be curious, mustering the forces of his knowledge but avoiding the disaster of that other battle he remembers so clearly. I do not see him ever underestimating the power of his enemy.